ELECTRONIC AND NEWER CERAMICS

ELECTRONIC

AND

NEWER CERAMICS

What They Are

How to Make Them

How They Are Used

PUBLISHED BY

INDUSTRIAL PUBLICATIONS, INC.

CHICAGO 3, ILLINOIS

Publishers of Technical Books   •   Journals and Business Literature
Ceramic Industry   •   Ceramic Data Book   •   Brick and Clay Record
Practical Builder   •   Dealers' Directory   •   Building Supply News
Building Construction Illustrated

iv

PREFACE

This book represents a survey of the basic concepts of the field generally known under the designation electronic and newer ceramics. It is a collection of material from the pages of CERAMIC INDUSTRY magazine and represents the work of a number of outstanding authorities in the field. It is designed to introduce the subject both to those already practicing ceramics and to students who will practice in the future. If it succeeds in this, the purpose of the authors and editors will have been fulfilled.

> J. J. SVEC
> GEORGE L. VINCENT
> KENNETH A. BRENT
> *Editors*

Chicago, Illinois
September, 1959

v

CONTENTS

CHAPTER I

AN INTRODUCTION TO ELECTRONIC CERAMICS

GEORGE L. VINCENT

Technical Editor, Ceramic Industry

The past 25 years have seen a phenomenal growth of the ceramic industries' newest division, electronic ceramics. Although considerable work had been done in the field prior to the advent of World War II, it was this holocaust which really sparked the research and development expenditures which brought electronic ceramics to a sizeable stature.

Ceramic products made under the classification of electronic ceramics depart radically from the conventional ceramic compositions and in so doing have created the necessity for the establishment of many new and highly refined manufacturing processes.

So virile was this youngest of the ceramic groups, and so extensive the possibilities for the uses of its products that its phenomenal growth did not stop with the end of World War II. Instead, its rate of growth continued to climb until today it is one of the most rapidly mushrooming industries in the economy. At present there is hardly a day that goes by without the announcement of some new electronic ceramic material, product or component and this avalanche makes it very difficult for anyone associated with the field to stay abreast of its developments.

CERAMIC INDUSTRY magazine, in its monthly publication, attempts to present a continuing series of articles on these new materials, products, processes, and in its special materials issues maintains a constant revision of the growing list of raw materials available to this specialized ceramic division.

With the publication of this book, CERAMIC INDUSTRY has paused to take a breath and is presenting here a review of much of the current knowledge in the field. It is our purpose in presenting this volume to provide information and data essential to anyone in the field of electronic ceramic manufacture or in the uses of its products. However, it is at once obvious that much of the knowledge herewith presented has already been added to; it is much like the present aircraft and missile industry—when the first prototype flies it has already become obsolete. The material presented here does not necessarily become obsolete, but it is to any reader's benefit to continue reading the Electronic and New Ceramics Section of CERAMIC INDUSTRY to supplement this book and to keep abreast of the current developments which are superseding material herewith presented.

CHAPTER II

TITANATES—AND WHAT THEY ARE

LARRY J. RUFFNER

Jeffers Electronics Division, Speer Carbon Co.

The past decade has seen the advent of a totally new and unique type of ceramic—the titanate. A great deal of time and effort have thus far gone into their development and investigation. Unfortunately, however, there remains quite a bit of controversy concerning the basic properties of titanate materials, and published reports on the subject conflict with one another as often as not. Investigators often find it difficult to duplicate their own results and impossible to duplicate those of others.

In view of the uncertainty of the exact basic properties of titanates themselves, then, these articles will deal instead with the basic materials involved, the unusual effects exhibited by titanates, the fabrication of titanate parts, and their commercial applications. The articles are non-technical in nature, and are designed to acquaint ceramists in other branches of the industry with this new ceramic.

Difficult to Define Titanates

It is difficult to define titanate materials, since the term is used loosely to include compounds of titania and other oxides, as well as titania itself. Zirconates are common additives to titanates, and are extremely useful in their manufacture. Compounds of the elements tin, niobium, cerium and tantalum have been investigated and found to have useful properties. Titanate compounds, themselves, are most commonly formed from oxides of Group II elements which have been reacted with titania. An important exception is lead, which, as will be discussed later, imparts important properties to certain titanate bodies.

The most outstanding features of titanate materials are their relatively high dielectric constants. The dielectric constant, or "K", of a material represents a ratio between the capacitance of two electrodes separated by the material and the capacitance of the same two electrodes separated by air. By comparison with most ceramic insulating materials which have dielectric constants in the neighborhood of 4 to 8, titanates have been formulated with K's in excess of 10,000. Thus these unique materials permit the fabrication of extremely small capacitors, and indeed lend themselves to the design of entire electric circuits on one small piece.

Close Control of Raw Materials

The first step in the manufacture of titanate parts begins with the close control of incoming raw materials. In addition to standard physical tests, raw materials must conform closely with rigid specifications concerning their electrical properties. This is usually accomplished by obtaining samples of available lots of material from the supplier, and after thorough testing, ordering from that lot of material which most closely conforms with the specifications. Titanates, generally speaking, are modifications of the compound barium titanate (BaTiO$_2$). The ideal molecular barium oxide: titanium oxide ratio is 1:1. Properly fired BaTiO$_2$ should have, at room temperature, a K of 1450–1550. An extreme deviation from this range would be immediate cause for rejection.

It is, of course, possible to "doctor" these raw materials in case of necessity, but control of these doctored materials may sometimes be difficult. A lot of barium titanate with too low a K value would suggest an excess of TiO$_2$ beyond the stoichiometric ratio, and such a lot of material could be doctored by the addition of barium carbonate to bring the K value up within the usable range. In such a case, however, one runs the risk of incomplete reaction during firing and the possibility of free barium oxide in the fired body. The presence of this compound becomes troublesome due to its tendency to react with water and carbon dioxide in the air and revert back to barium carbonate, whose presence causes high electric losses in the finished part.

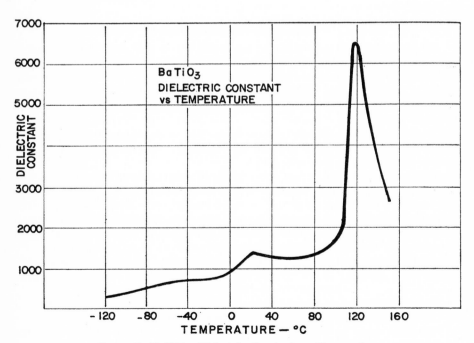

CHART I. BaTiO$_3$—Dielectric Constant vs. Temperature

Variation of K with Temperature

Another facet of the dielectric properties is the variation of K with temperature. This feature is capitalized upon in certain closely controlled bodies, which are fabricated and sold as temperature compensating parts. In higher K bodies, efforts are made to smooth out this variation as much as possible. Most bodies with K's in excess of 1,000 are composed primarily of barium titanate plus certain additives. Chart I is a graphical representation of K plotted against temperature for pure barium titanate. It will be noted that there is an extremely sharp peak in K at 120° C. for this material.

This peak, although modified, is carried into bodies containing barium titanate. The peak itself, which represents a transition in crystalline structure, is known as the Curie point. This peak can be made to shift in the direction of decreasing temperature by the addition of certain "shifter materials." It can then be modified further by other additions so as to flatten it out somewhat and cause a subsequent decrease in variation with temperature. It is, of course, possible to raise or lower the Curie point within certain limits with respect to K, but it usually follows that the higher K bodies have much steeper slopes, which, in turn, limits their usefulness to those applications which can tolerate a greater variation in K with temperature.

Polarizability Is Useful Property

Another useful property of certain titanate bodies is their polarizability. Two of the more common bodies suited for this kind of application contain barium titanate with minor additions of lead titanate or calcium titanate. Polarization results in their becoming piezoelectric, which effect gives them the ability to translate mechanical energy into electrical energy, and vice versa.

Titanate bodies may be divided into four commercial classes; the temperature compensating bodies mentioned earlier, the intermediate K bodies, the high K bodies and the piezoelectric bodies.

The nominal value of the temperature compensating type bodies represents a measure of the slope of the K-temperature curve within certain limits. Chart II demonstrates a series of temperature compensating bodies ranging from P 100 (positive slope, 100 parts/million parts/°C.) to N 750 (negative slope, 750 parts/million parts/°C.). It can be seen that the slope of the straight line allows the accurate prediction of K with temperature changes and that the changes themselves are constant.

Preparation of Bodies Demands Care

The preparation of these bodies, which can be accomplished in one of two ways, demands a great deal of care. For bodies with slopes between NPO (zero slope) and N 750, (negative, 750 parts/million/°C.) batch compositions represent a progressive shift in composition from one extreme to the other. The NPO body is composed primarily of BaTiO₂ and TiO₂ while the N 750 is essentially pure TiO₂. As additional TiO₂ is added to a composition its slope becomes progressively steeper. While the first method of preparation of these bodies involves direct batch formulation, the second method involves the blending of the two end products according to a predetermined ratio.

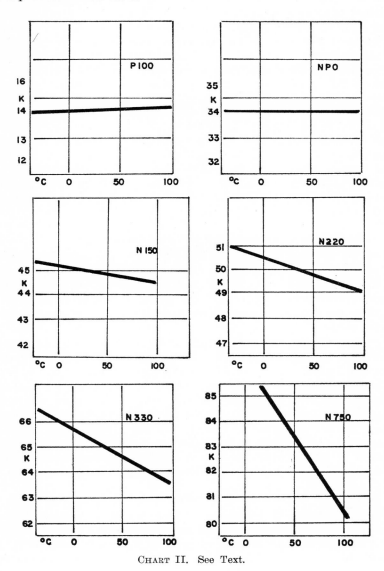

CHART II. See Text.

The advantage of the latter method lies in the fact that only the end products must be stored for use rather than the entire series of bodies. Inasmuch as the exact slopes of the end products are accurately measured before further use, it becomes much simpler to accurately formulate the intermediate products. All temperature compensating bodies, regardless of the method of preparation, must be tested for slope and adjusted if necessary before being approved for use. Bodies with slopes in excess of N 750 are formulated of other materials.

The intermediate K bodies are higher in barium titanate content and are more important for their higher K characteristics than for their temperature compensating characteristics. There is no distinct division between the intermediate K bodies and the higher K bodies, but they might arbitrarily be split at K 2000.

Effect on Curie Point

The high K bodies, although composed primarily of barium titanate, will contain some of the modifiers previously mentioned. Many of these bodies make use of the two-fold effect of strontium titanate, which serves to shift the Curie point further to the left (decreasing temperature) and raise the Curie point to a higher K value. Zirconate additions tend to shift the Curie point towards decreasing temperature ($BaZrO_3$, $CaZrO_3$, and $SrZrO_3$) or to drop the K ($MgZrO_3$).

The piezoelectric bodies usually fall into the intermediate K class with nominal values of K 1000 to K 1500, and are quite often prepared and sold as such.

CHAPTER III

PREPARING AND SHAPING TITANATE PARTS

Larry J. Ruffner

Jeffers Electronics Division, Speer Carbon Co.

The fact that titanate parts may be prepared by such standard methods as extruding, pressing or casting may convey the erroneous impression that they are as easily processed as more conventional ceramic compositions. In reality every phase of their preparation involves problems seldom encountered in the manufacture of most other ceramics. The principal difference arises from the fact that, whereas most ceramic bodies contain some clay which imparts plasticity to the material, titanate bodies contain no clay or other natural plasticizing materials. The problem of plasticity is complicated, too, by the fact that binders and plasticizers must be selected which will burn out of the part completely and have no adverse effect upon the fired density or the ultimate electrical properties. These materials must be as carefully tested and selected as the basic raw materials themselves.

Extreme Care in Processing

After acceptance of the binders, plasticizers and basic raw materials, extreme care must be exercised throughout all phases of processing to insure proper batch formulation, extremely intimate mixing of batch ingredients, and elimination of all possible sources of contamination. Generally, the first step in processing is ball-milling of the batch ingredients. Some manufacturers insist upon a wet-milling operation, while others find they can produce a satisfactory product with dry milling. There is much to be said for the wet milling process, however, since it insures a finer-grained structure and a subsequently higher density. It also insures the removal of troublesome spots in the finished product, which are often the focal point of voltage breakdowns and other electrical failures. Pieces produced from wet-milled materials are generally considered superior in quality and appearance.

The preparation of extrusion material usually involves the addition of water soluble plasticizers plus sufficient extra water to bring the mix to an extrusion consistency. Mixing may be accomplished in muller type mixers or in double arm type mixers. Both have their advantages: the muller type mixer is more efficient in rapidly obtaining uniform moisture distribution, while the double arm type is more adaptable to temperature control by the use of water jackets. Temperature control is helpful due to a tendency of the material to heat up during mixing, which sometimes causes it to become stiffer and more difficult to mix.

Control tests must be run to insure perfectly even moisture distribution and the proper percentage of water before the material is approved for extrusion.

Extrusion Dies Are Critical

Due to the close tolerances which are usually demanded of titanate parts, extrusion dies must be of the finest workmanship. Some manufacturers find too great a tendency of the pin forming the internal dimensions to "float," and resort to one-piece dies of special design to eliminate this trouble. Most extruded titanates demonstrate a certain amount of thixotropy which manifests itself as a result of the work expended in forcing it through the die, and consequently the extruded ware must be handled with extreme care to avoid any deformation. Extruded parts may be dried by placing them in V-shaped troughs on plaster batts and air-drying them in a clean room. After thorough drying, the extruded ware is cut to size by multiple cutters. The extruded ware is then carefully cleaned of cutting dust and loaded onto high-temperature refractory setters for firing. These setters must be of some material inert to the action of titanates during firing. Common materials used include barium zirconate, calcium zirconate, zirconium oxide, and sometimes alumina.

Dry Pressing Commonly Used

Probably the most common method of forming titanates is dry pressing. One process concerns itself with the preparation of granules from material which contains water soluble binders and plasticizers and a closely controlled water content. In this process, the damp material (approximately 3% water) is placed in sealed jars which are then heated (or "sweated") to induce uniform moisture content. One serious disadvantage of this process is a tendency of the material to cake together. The more common method of forming dry press materials involves the addition of waxes, either in emulsion or solution.

Some manufacturers, using emulsions, feed their "slip" directly into spray dryers, which yield a spherical dry grain ready for pressing, while others prefer to dry the material after the wax addition and form the grain mechanically. The latter method involves controlled crushing of the dry wax-impregnated material, and careful separation of the desired grain fraction. One advantage of the wax being introduced in solution lies in the higher green strength of parts pressed from this type grain. A serious disadvantage, however, are the undesirable properties of most of the solvents available: obnoxious odors, inflammability, toxic fumes, etc.

Whereas extrusion lends itself primarily to the production of tubes, dry pressing is best suited to the production of discs and retangular plates. One inherent disadvantage in the dry pressing of titanates is the extreme difficulty encountered in pressing thicker parts. Since these materials do not flow as well under pressure as most ceramic bodies, conditions sometimes arise where the outside of a piece is pressed more densely than the inside, and cracks result upon firing.

Casting Is Difficult Process

Casting is probably the most difficult method of forming titanate parts. The structure of cast ware, although presumably very dense, is weak, and most manufacturers have their own secret formulae for imparting additional strength to the cast ware. At best, however, cast parts are on the weak side, and considerable care must be exercised in trimming or handling. One of the more efficient processes is centrifugal casting in which a measured amount of slip of known specific gravity is charged into a mold which is then rotated until sufficient water has been removed to allow the materials to build up on the walls and form the piece. Contrary to expectations, some experimenters have found it more difficult to properly mature cast titanate ware than extruded or dry pressed ware. In some cases, the addition of a small amount of beryllia or zinc oxide is helpful in maturing cast ware, but their effect upon the ultimate electrical properties of the bodies must be considered.

Another manufacturing method being used, particularly in the preparation of extremely thin pieces of titanate, is the "doctor-blade" method. It derives its name from a horizontally mounted steel blade which is drawn across a puddle of titanate slip, smoothing it out to a uniform thickness. The height of each end of the blade is controlled with micrometer adjustments, and may be set so as to produce pieces with thicknesses down to 0.005". The slip employs plastic binders dissolved in fast-drying solvents, and the resulting films rapidly dry to flexible sheets, which may be sliced or stamped to the desired sizes.

Firing procedures exert a profound influence upon the ultimate physical and electrical properties of titanate compositions. Inasmuch as titania-containing compounds are particularly sensitive to reducing conditions caused by residual carbon or kiln atmosphere, many manufacturers have found their task made easier by the use of electrically fired kilns, whose oxidizing atmospheres serve to minimize problems resulting from reduced ware. This does not necessarily imply that gas fired kilns cannot be used—their use merely necessitates a closer control of atmosphere. Indeed, there are those who feel that gas firing of titanates is superior to electrical firing, since the binders and plasticizers are more readily burned away in the pre-heat zone.

Have Wide Firing Range

Titanates have a remarkably wide firing range. Many compositions can be fired over a 300° F. range. As a very general rule, however, an increase in firing temperature yields an increase in K value, and most manufacturers find it advisable to fire near the top of this range to insure proper density and the desired K. Too low a firing temperature may result in a very slight amount of porosity which cannot be tolerated because of the high electrical losses which invariably result.

It is generally accepted that extremely fine crystallization is preferred over coarser crystals in titanate because of the superior electrical properties imparted by the former. It is the firing cycle which controls this crystal structure to a large degree. The pre-heating and firing parts of the cycle are relatively unimportant and may be accomplished as rapidly as possible, so long as the parts are properly oxidized to remove the binder, and are properly matured. Once matured, the parts should be cooled rapidly in order to prevent the aforementioned crystal growth. For this reason the cooling part of the cycle is considered the most critical.

Samples Tested in Lab

Samples of every fired lot of titanate parts are delivered to the electrical testing laboratory where they are tested for dielectric constant values, power factor, and, in some cases, temperature compensating characteristics, aging effect (effect of time on dielectric constant), and accelerated life tests. While electrical tests are being conducted, the remaining parts are inspected physically for chips, cracks, spots, camber, and concentricity.

After each lot passes inspection it is then ready for fabrication into completed capacitor units. Since all parts are to be used in electrical circuits, they must first receive their electrodes. These electrodes consist of two metallic films on opposite surfaces of the ceramic; the films and the ceramic dielectric separating them comprising the capacitor. Electrodes are applied by hand painting, spraying, stenciling, or silk-screening patterns of silver paste onto the parts; which are then passed through a small electric kiln operating at about 1400° F. in order to fire on the silver patterns.

Simple capacitors are then ready to receive their mounting leads, which may be soldered on mechanically or by hand. Printed circuit patterns are completed by the application of resistor material, and soldering of leads. All completed units are sealed by the application of suitable wax or plastic combinations.

Treatment For Piezoelectric Units

All units intended for piezoelectric applications are set aside for further treatment after they have received their silver patterns and leads. This treatment consists of the application of a high D.C. potential across the piece. While some manufacturers find they obtain higher activity constants by first heating the part and then cooling it through the Curie point while the voltage is being applied, others find they can obtain comparable results by performing the operation at room temperature. In either case, the high voltages required dictate that the operation be carried out in a suitable insulating liquid medium to reduce the possibility of flashover. Pieces so polarized demonstrate unusual effects in that they will generate a small but usable current upon the application of pressure. Conversely, the application of an A.C. voltage across the electrodes will cause the piece to vibrate and transform the electrical energy into mechanical energy.

CHAPTER IV

APPLICATIONS OF TITANATES

LARRY J. RUFFNER

Jeffers Electronics Division, Speer Carbon Co.

The preceding articles of this series have concerned themselves with a discussion of titanate materials and some of the methods used in fabricating them into usable parts. Both articles were designed to stress the care which must be exercised throughout their manufacture. It was intended that the articles be of a non-technical nature, directed toward workers in other branches of the ceramic industry. For this reason, only the more important points were touched upon. For this same reason, this article will confine itself to the more common uses made of titanates.

As a general rule, manufactured titanate ceramics will fall into one of two general categories—capacitor units or piezoelectric units.

Used Widely in Capacitors

Capacitor units (or condensers) represent the bulk of titanate manufacture. In addition to being used as direct replacements for mica and paper type condensers in many existing circuits, they are being selected over other type units in many new designs.

One of the major advantages of titanate capacitors, as was mentioned in an earlier article, lies in their relatively small sizes. The size-capacity relationship of any capacitor may be expressed by the equation

$$C = \frac{KA}{bT}$$

where C = Capacity
$\qquad$ K = Dielectric Constant
$\qquad$ T = Thickness of dielectric
$\qquad$ A = Effective electrode area
$\qquad$ b = Numerical Constant

Inasmuch as the capacity is directly proportional to the dielectric constant and the area, an increase in dielectric constant allows a decrease in area, and consequently, a smaller piece. The capacity of any capacitor may likewise be increased by a decrease in the thickness. The higher dielectric strength (resistance to electrical breakdown) of titanate materials permits a greater decrease in the thickness than is possible with many other dielectrics, and consequently, the attainment of even higher capacitances.

Many Designs; One Principle

Titanate capacitors lend themselves to many designs, but the basic principle involved is always the same—the separation of two electrodes by a dielectric medium. The more common shapes are tubes, discs, and rectangular plates.

Tubular capacitors are made by the application of silver electrodes on the inside and outside walls of titanate tubes. The more common of these units are about ⅛" in diameter and ⅝" long. A variation of the tubular condenser is the trimmer condenser which has a standard silver electrode on the outside wall, while the inside of the tube is threaded to receive a metal screw. The screw, in this case, acts as an electrode; and the depth to which it is turned in or out determines the effective electrode area and therefore the capacitance of the unit.

Disc type capacitors will commonly measure from ⅛" to 1.0" in diameter and from 0.015" to 0.050" in thickness. Like the tubular type, they may be simple capacitors or may be made into trimmers. The trimmers may be made by silvering one half of one face and mounting the piece, pattern up, over a base with the same type pattern. As the disc is rotated on its mounting screw, the electrode area changes, and with it, the capacitance.

Rectangular plates may be made into either single or multiple capacitors. Printed circuit components are an example of the latter. These units, along with the disc and tubular type capacitors, find widespread use in radio, television, and radar units where space limitations must be met.

Use of Piezoelectric Titanate Parts

The limited use of piezoelectric titanate parts is attributable, in part, at least, to industry's general unfamiliarity with this product and its potential uses. Those industries which had previously made use of piezoelectric materials such as Rochelle Salts and quartz crystals were quick to seize upon the several advantages offered by titanate materials. Whereas Rochelle salts cannot withstand water or heat, titanates are unaffected by water and have greater temperature stability. Quartz crystals must be cut from natural crystalline formations or artificially grown—a costly process in either case. Titanate materials may be formed into very intricate shapes at little more cost than any other ceramic.

One of the more important applications of piezoelectric titanate parts is in sonar (underwater submarine detection) apparatus. The heart of this apparatus is a titanate unit which is able to translate the mechanical energy of underwater sound or vibration into electrical energy. These units are placed in water and each unit utilizes its self-contained radio transmitter in relaying information back to a central control, which is then able to pinpoint underwater disturbances with a high degree of accuracy. Submarines also make use of similar devices in transmitting and receiving messages among themselves.

The same type of unit is also being used quite successfully by the fishing industry in locating schools of fish.

Wide Use in Phonograph Pickups

Another widespread use of piezoelectric titanate is the use of polarized crystalline units in phonograph pickups. The vibrations set up by the needle riding over the phonograph record are transmitted to the crystal unit inside the tone arm. The crystal unit converts these vibrations accurately and efficiently into electrical impulses which are in turn amplified and fed into the loudspeaker. The same principle is applied and used in crystal microphones, where the diaphragm transmits the mechanical (sound) energy to the crystal unit. As in the phonograph pickup, the unit converts this mechanical energy into electrical.

The preceding examples have been those in which mechanical energy is converted into electrical energy. There are, however, instances where the process is reversed, and electrical energy is changed into mechanical. For example, much of the work being done today in the field of ultrasonics makes use of titanate units which can be made to vibrate at ultrasonic frequencies by the application of electricity.

High intensity has been found to work very well in certain mixing operations. Its use has been found to hasten certain chemical reactions, and it is also used both in preparing or coagulating dispersions and emulsions.

Another commercial application of polarized titanates is to be found in certain cleaning operations where high frequency energy is utilized in removing boiler scale, cleaning ball bearing assemblies, etc.

Ability to Focus Transmitted Energy

One of the properties of piezoelectric titanates which makes them very well suited for many of their uses is their ability to focus their transmitted energy. This, of course, is accomplished in the design of the piece. For example, the focus of a vibrating tube coincides with the longitudinal axis of the tube; while in the case of a spherical segment, the energy is focused in the same manner as is light from a spherical mirror.

Although the titanates, relatively speaking, are in their infancy and much work remains to be done, they have already taken a prominent and permanent place in both ceramics and electronics industries.

CHAPTER V

CERAMICS FOR THERMAL SHOCK RESISTANCE

F. A. Hummel
Pennsylvania State University

A. *Definition*

It is very difficult to define a thermal shock resistant ceramic except to say that it is a composition which does not fail under the thermal stress which is developed during some stated temperature cycling process.

For example, porcelain teeth made of a feldspathic composition do not fail due to the stresses developed by cycling between ice cream and hot coffee temperatures. Under these conditions the body may be considered thermal shock resisting. However, feldspathic tooth porcelain is actually not a very thermal shock resistant type of ceramic and it would probably fail if cycled over a 0-400° C. temperature interval, using liquids as cooling and heating media.

In these modern times we are more inclined to think of a thermal shock resisting material as one which withstands the rigors of temperature cycling demanded by jet aircraft turbine blades where temperature differences of at least 1000° C. are generated in only a few moments of time.

Thus, from these two examples of extreme cases, we see that the term "thermal shock resisting material" is not well defined and that one must at least state the conditions of test and the size and shape of the body to be tested before any estimate can be made of the probable success of any given ceramic body type, based on the physical constants of the materials in the body.

B. *The Need for These Materials*

1. *Refractories*—As indicated above, the greatest single stimulation toward the development of materials with great thermal shock resistance has come from the aircraft industry, with special emphasis on turbine blades, combustion chambers, rocket nozzles and other special parts of jet and rocket devices. Many general papers on the requirements for these special refractory applications have appeared in the past decade, but few answers have yet been obtained and much research is still being done in this field.

Many new applications for special thermal shock resisting refractories have arisen which are entirely outside the realm of the aircraft industry. The general problem of refractories for the combustion of fuels has turned in a new direction. Burner tips, nozzles, tubes and special parts are required which will permit faster or more efficient burning.

Crucibles for Metallurgical Industry

Special crucibles are needed for the metallurgical industry to contain the newer metals which in turn are desired for their corrosion and thermal

14

shock resistant properties. Nuclear engineering requires refractories which can resist molten metals and salts which are used as coolants in the atomic pile. Even the atomic fuel elements are desired in thermal shock resisting forms.

In addition to these newer demands for special refractories there remains the old problems in improving the spalling resistance of the conventional refractories which make up the bulk of industrial production.

There is always the search for improved spalilng resistance in silica, alumina, fireclay, chrome, magnesite, mullite,[1] zircon and other standard brick made by the refractories industry.

Needs Vary in Whiteware Industries

2. *Whiteware*—In this segment of the industry, which includes porcelain teeth, wall tile, floor tile, vitrified and semivitreous dinnerware, sanitaryware, high and low voltage electrical porcelain, chemical porcelain and the borderline field of spark plug porcelains, the need for materials of greater thermal shock resistance varies widely. The first four types of bodies mentioned above are, in general, presently satisfactory with respect to thermal shock resistance, since no special demands are made on these wares from a temperature cycling standpoint.

There is no doubt, however, that the manufacturers of sanitaryware, electrical porcelain and chemical porcelain are alert for the development of more thermal shock resistant qualities in their wares, although the urgency is not of the same order of magnitude as it is in the special refractories field.

With regard to spark plugs, this item is so closely tied to the aircraft industry that the production of new types of plugs has been absolutely essential. Although the final products have been achieved by adjustment of compositions and considerable ingenuity in engineering and design,[2,3] the thermal shock resistant requirement has always been a prominent factor.

Uses in Electronic Devices

3. *Electronics*—Barium titanate and its derivatives (including niobates, zirconates and stannates) steatite, zircon, forsterite, wollastonite and glass-bonded mica products are typical of the bodies now used for condensers, coil forms, bushings and a wide variety of other applications in the electronic industries.

For most of these applications the thermal shock resistance of these bodies is satisfactory, particularly since the size of the items is usually small and the cycling not severe. Nevertheless, the performance of steatite, forsterite and wollastonite porcelains is strictly borderline when thermal shock resistance is considered. One of the reasons why zircon is competitive with steatite in the high frequency field is its improved thermal shock resistance.

4. *Glass*—Some of the most excellent thermal shock resisting materials are available from the glass industry, including fused silica, Vycor and Pyrex brand glasses. However, for some applications these materials are difficult to shape to precision requirements and in addition they may soften or crystallize on exposure to elevated temperatures.

It is difficult to visualize what glass composition would give the low expansion properties of fused silica glass, yet be higher melting and more resistant to deformation and crystallization. Yet this product may appear in the future.

Thermal Shock Resistance in Abrasives

5. *Abrasives*—Grinding wheels are composed of an abrasive grain such as corundum or silicon carbide, bonded by an organic resin, a glass or other crystalline material. These combinations must obviously withstand the thermal shocks which arise when the wheel is cutting through very hard metal or nonmetallic products in service. The abrasive industry therefore is seeking improved thermal shock resisting bonds and better over-all thermal shock resistance in the finished wheel.

6. *Glass-to-Metal and Ceramic-to-Metal*—Porcelain enamel has had to deal with thermal shocks ranging from those experienced by the common pot and pan to very severe stress encountered in the huge glassed steel vats used by the chemical and food processing industries. The art of sealing to various metals [4] and the development of so-called "solder glasses" has led to groups of composite metal-to-glass units which are in many cases relatively resistant to thermal shock. The same can be said for ceramic-to-metal seals which are being treated in separate articles in this series.

In conclusion, it is safe to say that almost every manufacturer of ceramic bodies will welcome a more thermal shock resistant product, providing the electrical, mechanical, optical and thermal properties are unaltered. Many of them are hard at work trying to develop compositions with greater shock resistance.

Historical Development

A. *Early History*

The first experiments designed to test thermal shock resistance or "thermal endurance" were recorded by Winkelmann and Schott [5] in 1894. These workers used a variety of glass compositions, tested them over a very limited temperature range and evolved a simple relation between thermal endurance (Θ) and several physical properties of the material namely,

$$\Theta = \frac{S.k}{E.a}$$

where S = tensile strength
k = thermal conductivity
E = modulus of elasticity
a = coefficient of thermal expansion

That the relationship appeared in such a simple form was due to the fact that small glass rods of homogeneous composition were cycled over a very limited temperature range. The general case of thermal shock resistance leads to a much more complicated relationship involving not only the material constants mentioned above, but also a heat transfer coefficient and a "size and shape" factor.

More Work on Thermal Endurance

Subsequent papers [6] took these latter factors into account, and the work on thermal endurance of glass continued with contributions by Stott, Knapp, Gould and Hampton, Warren, Tabata and Moriya, Schonbörn, Murgatroyd and Clark.

In a recent paper by Karkhanavala and Scholes,[7] the authors reviewed the many contributions to the literature on the thermal endurance of glass and developed a relationship between this property and the diameter of glass rods for several different chemical compositions. The final equation is presented in the following form:

$$\Theta = \frac{\sigma(1\text{-}\mu)}{E.a} \, (1 + 3 \, [0.6])^{r/r_1}$$

where σ = modulus of rupture

μ = Poisson's ratio

E = modulus of elasticity

a = coefficient of thermal expansion

r = radius of the rod (m.m.)

r_1 = unit radius (m/m)

B. *Present Status*

Although much of the early work was concerned with the thermal endurance of glass due to the ease of testing homogeneous rods or spheres over small temperature intervals, the bulk of the current work in this field has been stimulated by the need for high temperature refractory parts for aircraft. Consequently, the experimental procedures have expanded to include crystalline materials, combinations of glassy and crystalline ceramic bodies, tests which are made over a wide range of temperatures and heat transfer conditions, and a great variety of test shapes of widely differing porosities and thermal conductivities.

Moreover, at the present stage of development, much use is being made of the theory of stress, elasticity and heat flow in the generation of general equations for thermal shock resistance. The concept of a thermal shock resistivity is becoming more sharply defined.

Definitions and Background

A. *Definitions and Factors*

"Thermal shock resistance" is defined as the resistance to weakening or fracture due to a sudden transient temperature change. Thermal shock gives rise to thermal stresses due to the difference in expansion (or contraction) of various parts of a body such that free expansion of each small increment of volume cannot take place.

The thermal shock resistance is a function of a large number of factors which can conveniently be divided into two groups, (1) those factors which are physical constants for the material under consideration, such as strength, elasticity, coefficient of expansion and thermal conductivity and (2) those factors which are peculiar to the test procedure such as heat transfer coefficient, size and shape of the specimen and interaction with the heating and cooling medium.

B. *Influence of Body Texture*

The ideal case deals with the homogeneous isotropic body (glass or cubic crystal) whose physical properties do not vary with temperature. Only in rare cases do we find these ideal conditions and the most general case involves a heterogeneous body containing anisotropic constituents whose physical properties do vary with temperature.

With respect to physical texture, some cases which arise are shown schematically in Fig. 1.

In Fig. 1, case 1 is the ideal, since no grain boundaries or interfaces are involved. Case 2 illustrates the single oxide body composed of anistotropic crystals and grain boundaries along which stress can develop due simply to a variation of thermal expansion coefficient with crystallographic direction. Cases 3, 4, 5, 6 and 7 represent the more complicated possibilities where at least two phases are present with subsequent interfacial layers or grain boundaries producing areas whose physical properties are not as well defined as those of the two primary constituents. Naturally, the relative proportion of continuous to discontinuous phase has considerable influence on the thermal shock behavior in these bodies. If neither phase is

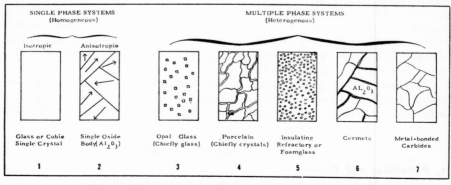

Fig. 1. Some possible variations in physical texture of thermal shock resistant materials (schematic).

continuous, the nature of the distribution of the two phases becomes very important. The situation becomes most complex if a glass or metal is used to bond two or more crystalline materials, particularly if vigorous interaction takes place during the first firing or heat treatment of the body.

In the case of the multiphase composition it is obviously extremely difficult, if not sometimes impossible, to determine the influence of the four basic physical properties of each phase on the thermal shock resistance of the composite body. In addition, as stated previously, the interface makes an undetermined but very critical contribution to behavior of the system.

C. *Influence of Testing Procedure*

Stresses in a homogeneous ceramic body can arise even though the body is at a uniform temperature. This is the case of the polycrystalline body containing anisotropic crystals or the multiphase body, (Fig. I, cases 2 to 7) where the origin of the stress lies in the anisotropy of thermal expansion characteristics.

In the more general case, the stress arises from thermal gradients. In calculating thermal gradients, two important cases arise, the steady state condition or the unsteady state transient condition. The former case is usually a simpler one, since the temperature distribution is determined by the rate of heat flow, the shape of the specimen and the thermal conductivity. In unsteady state calculations, the time variable enters the calculation. In the unsteady state testing method, two cases are generally recognized, (1) the heat transfer coefficient is infinite and (2) the heat transfer coefficient is constant.

D. *Expression of Resistance*

From the recent intensive study and correlation of thermal shock test data [8] it becomes apparent that it is not possible to list one single factor or index which can characterize "thermal shock resistance." Analytical expressions for the thermal shock resistance require the use of two parameters in the most general case. For low rates of heat transfer, the maximum temperature difference (ΔT_{max}) which the material can stand is proportional to:

$$\frac{k.S}{E\,a} (1 - \mu)$$

where k = thermal conductivity
S = strength
μ = Poisson's ratio
E = modulus of elasticity
a = coefficient of expansion

For high rates of heat transfer,

$$\Delta T_{max} :: \frac{S}{E\,a} (1 - \mu)$$

For example, for an infinite slab,

$$\Delta \, T_{max} = \frac{S}{E. \, a}\left(1 + \frac{4K}{aH} \right)$$

where a = shape factor
where H = heat transfer coefficient

The factor which does not include the thermal conductivity is designated R, while the factor which does include k is designated R^1.

An excellent extended account of the basis for the equation, thermal shock test methods and the factors affecting thermal shock testing can be found in reference 8.

REFERENCES FOR CHAPTER V

1. "Crystallite," Bulletin CR-11, Richard C. Remmey Son Co., Philadelphia 37, Pa.
2. F. H. Riddle, "Ceramic Spark-Plug Insulators," Jour. Amer. Cer. Soc., 32 (11) p. 333 (1949).
3. T. G. McDougal, "History of AC Spark Plug Division, General Motors Corporation," Bull. Amer. Cer. Soc. 38 (11) p. 445 (1949).
4. Louis Navias, "Advances in Ceramics Related to Electronic Tube Development," Jour. Amer. Cer. Soc. 37 (8), p. 329–50 (August 1954).
5. Winkelmann, A., and Schott, O., "Über thermische Widerstandscoefficienten verschiedener Glaser in ihrer Abbangigkeit von der chemischen Zusammensetzung," Ann. Physik und Chem., 51, 730 (1894).
6. Hovestadt, H., "Jenaer Glas. Verlag von Gustav Fischer," Jena 1900, p. 225.
7. Karkhanavala, M. D., and Scholes, S. R., "The Relation Between Diameter and Thermal Endurance of Glass Rods," Jour. Soc. Glass Tech., 35 (107) 289–303T (1951).
8. "Symposium on Thermal Fracture," Jour. Amer. Cer. Soc. 38 (1), January 1955.

CHAPTER VI

FACTORS IN CERAMICS' RESISTANCE TO THERMAL SHOCK

F. A. HUMMEL
Pennsylvania State University

Factors Affecting Resistance

A. *Strength*

The types of strength measurements which can be made on glass or ceramic compositions are : Tensile, torsion, shear, bending and compressive. In general, data are not available for ceramic materials in torsion or in shear tests, although the shear strength is often taken as two to four times the tensile strength.

Compressive strengths are highest for glass and ceramic bodies, amounting to 100,000 lbs./sq. in. for a dense alumina body, for example. Data on tensile strengths are much in demand by designers of thermal shock resisting components and in recent years an increasing number of useful figures have appeared in the literature, due to the extensive research programs undertaken by the Bureau of Standards,[9] several research institutes and universities and the industrial laboratories.

The reason for the lack of data on tensile strengths is partly the difficulty involved in making homogeneous test specimens which are dimensionally accurate and partly the difficulty of the tensile test itself. Failure may occur due to stress concentration in the grips or to torsional stresses in the sample resulting from poor alignment.

Condition of Surface Important

In testing the strength of glasses, the condition of the surface is extremely important. Freshly drawn glass fibers have exceedingly high strengths, whereas abraded surfaces of large diameter glass rods may yield only 5,000 p.s.i. in flexural tests.

The strength of bodies composed of a large amount of glass phase with some crystalline materials suspended in the glass can be influenced by heat treatment in much the same manner as homogeneous glass compositions.[10] The strength of bodies containing relatively small amounts of glass phase can also be influenced (improved) by heat treatment, but in the two latter cases it must be remembered that relaxation of stress will occur during thermal shock treatment.

The strength of most crystalline materials is but little affected by thermal stressing, although in some cases this effect can be amplified to a marked degree.

21

Flexural Test Determines Strength

In general, the flexural test is most often used as the criterion of the strength of glasses or ceramic bodies. The flexural test can give values of strength which are equal to the tensile strength of the material under consideration or, as is more often the case, values which are about three times that of the actual tensile strength.

The transverse strength of ceramic bodies may be varied about tenfold in the case of thermal shock resisting materials. Some relatively weak bodies may give strengths as low as 4500 p.s.i. while sintered alumina is among the strongest known at 45,000 p.s.i. Table I gives some representative values of strength for a variety of ceramic bodies.

B. *Elasticity*

The modulus of elasticity of dense ceramic materials is capable of only a fivefold (approximately) variation at room temperature and in general, the value of E for any given body composition does not change appreciably at 800° C. In this temperature range ceramic materials are very brittle and obey Hooke's law up to the rupture stress. At elevated

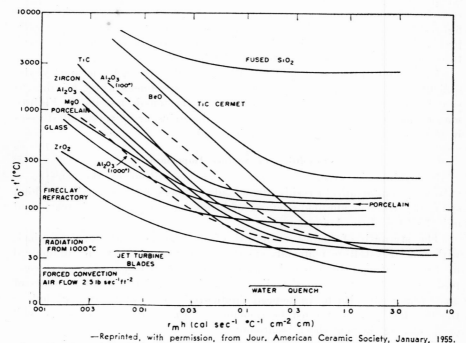

—Reprinted, with permission, from Jour. American Ceramic Society, January, 1955.

FIG. 2. Variation in maximum quenching temperature with different rates of heat transfer. Calculated from material properties at 400° C. Dashed curves for Al_2O_3 calculated from material properties at 100° C. and 1000° C.

TABLE I

Transverse strength of ceramic bodies

Body Type	Transverse Strength, p.s.i.
Lithium Aluminosilicate	7,000
Cordierite	8,000
Porcelain	10,000
Mullite	13,000
Zircon	15,000 and up
Forsterite	20,000
Dense Alumina	45,000
TiC cermet	60,000

temperatures, glass-bonded or metal-bonded ceramic bodies (or cermets) exhibit plastic flow which no doubt improves the resistance to thermal shock. If deformation of the material does not take place, this effect may be used to great advantage in certain cases.

Table II gives some representative values of the E modulus and Poisson's ratio for selected ceramic compositions:

In general as the strength of a ceramic material increases, so does the value of the E modulus, thereby working against one another as far as their effect on improving thermal shock resistance is concerned.

TABLE II

Elastic properties of ceramic bodies

Body Type	E, lb./sq. in. x 10^6	Mu
Porcelain	10	0.30
Mullite	21	0.30
Zircon	20	0.35
Spinel	34	0.31
Dense Al_2O_3	51	0.20
TiC cermet	60	0.30

C. *Thermal Expansion Coefficient*

The thermal expansion coefficient of a ceramic body may be defined as as a linear coefficient,

$$a_L = \frac{1}{L} \frac{dl}{dT}$$

or a volume coefficient,

$$a_V = \frac{1}{V} \frac{dV}{dT}$$

It is most commonly measured on randomly oriented ceramic aggregates in the form of bars or rods 3 to 7 inches long, thereby yielding a linear coefficient. This material property is capable of one of the greatest variations (at least 50 fold) of all the inherent material properties of a glass or crystal, since some glasses and crystals show virtually no change in dimensions with temperature, while others may have linear expansion coefficients well over $200 \times 10^{-7} cm/cm/°$ C.

The expansion coefficient probably exerts the most important influence on thermal shock resistance of all body properties, since the unexcelled behavior of fused silica, Vycor brand glass or beta spodumene type crystalline ceramic bodies is well known to all who have had occasion to use these materials in the form of crucibles or other special shapes.

In a later section, specific ceramic bodies will be discussed in groups, classified according to their thermal expansion coefficients since this property probably provides the best single index to the thermal shock resistance of body compositions.

Expansion Coefficients of Glasses

Karkhanavala[11] has provided the glass industry with a recent compilation of the thermal expansion coefficients of many glasses. Even now this compilation is relatively incomplete due to the many glass compositions whose expansions have been determined since 1952. Unfortunately no such compilation is available for crystalline materials. However a convenient summary of the average expansion coefficient for several common ceramic materials is given in Table III.

Beta-eucryptite is included in the table to indicate that some crystalline materials may occasionally be expected to show a thermal contraction

TABLE III
Coefficient of thermal expansion of ceramic materials

Material	Coefficient of Expansion $\alpha \times 10^{-7}$
β—Eucryptite	-60 (to 700° C.)
β—Spodumene	<5
Fused Silica	5
Vycor Glass	8
Aluminum Titanate	<10 (to 1000° C.)
Zirconium Phosphate	<10 (to 700° C.)
Cordierite	20
Beryl	20
SnO_2	
Silicon Carbide	35
Mullite	40
Zircon	40
$BeO, Al_2O_3, BeAl_2O_4, MgAl_2O_4$	80–90
Cubic ZrO_2	110
MgO, CaO	140

rather than the normally anticipated thermal expansion behavior. For a more extended discussion of thermal expansion and its relation to the structure and behavior of ceramic materials the reader is referred to three recent papers [12, 13, 14] on this subject.

D. *Thermal Conductivity*

The thermal conductivity of ceramic materials can exhibit the greatest variation of all material properties. At room temperature a 100 fold difference can exist between porcelain bodies and graphite as shown in Table IV. At 800 or 1000° C. the variation in thermal conductivity between different types of ceramic materials is much less marked and may involve only a factor of 10.

TABLE IV
Thermal conductivity of ceramic materials

Material	k (cal. sec.$^{-1}$ °C.$^{-1}$ cm.$^{-2}$ cm.)	
	100° C.	1000° C.
Fused silica	.0038	....
Porcelain	.0041	.0045
Mullite	.015	.010
Zircon	.016	.010
Spinel	.036	.014
Alumina	.072	.015
TiC cermet	.083	....
Graphite	.426	.149
BeO	.525	.049

When the temperature interval over which thermal shock is being tested is small (ca. 100° C.), the thermal conductivity can be taken as essentially constant. However, for large variations in temperature such as those involved in radiant heat transfer (fourth power of the absolute temperature) the large change in k should be taken into consideration by the investigator.

Coble and Kingery [8] have studied the effect of porosity on the thermal stress resistance of sintered alumina bodies and found that the resistance to thermal stresses at 50% porosity is about one-third of that estimated for zero porosity. This will probably be found to be the trend for all pure oxide bodies which develop high strength and improve their thermal conductivity considerably on sintering to near the theoretical density.

Does Increase in Porosity Help?

It has been thought in the past that heterogeneous bodies such as sagger bodies improve their thermal shock properties with increase in porosity. However, this is a special case due to the texture of the body and the relatively slow rate of heating in tunnel or periodic kilns.

For a complete analysis of the thermal conductivity of ceramic bodies and methods of measurement, one should consult the collected papers from the Massachusetts Institute of Technology on this subject.[20]

To summarize for the four basic body properties, the greatest variation at room temperature can be made in the thermal conductivity, with thermal expansion, strength and modulus of elasticity being affected in decreasing order. For high rates of heat transfer during thermal shock the thermal conductivity k becomes relatively unimportant. The thermal expansion coefficient probably has the greatest influence on thermal shock behavior. The discussion now turns to size and shape.

E. Size and Shape

1. *Size*—It is obvious that the size of a ceramic body being subjected to thermal shock cycling will influence its behavior. One can consider extreme cases such as high voltage porcelain insulators which are 6 feet high and 2 to 3 feet in diameter versus spark plus, porcelain teeth and laboratory porcelain crucibles whose largest dimension is no more than 3 inches. In thermal stressing the large high voltage insulator only the surface temperature is altered and the behavior is relatively independent of the thermal conductivity and the rate of heat transfer. In heating a thin-walled porcelain crucible the entire body very quickly assumes the same average temperature. For the many cases which arise each has to be considered in the light of the service condition expected.

2. *Shape*—Kingery [4] has provided a summary of the surface and center stresses in various shapes. For simple shapes such as infinite slab, thin plates, thin disks, long solid cylinders, long hollow cylinders, solid spheres, hollow spheres, bricks and toroids (rings), the mathematical treatment is highly developed and can be applied to many actual cases. Baroody, Simons and Duckworth have made extensive experiments in the case of the hollow cylinder of circular and noncircular cross section.

TABLE V (after Kingery)

Values of surface heat-transfer coefficient, h

Conditions	h (B. t. u. hr.[1] °F[-1] Ft.[-2])	h (cal. sec.[-1] °C[-1] cm.[-2])
Air flow past cylinder:		
Flow rate 60 lb. sec.[-1] ft.[-2]	190	.026
Flow rate 25 lb. sec.[-1] ft.[-2]	90	.012
Flow rate 2.5 lb. sec.[-1] ft.[-2]	20	.0027
Flow rate 0.25 lb. sec.[-1] ft.[-2]	2	.00027
Radiation to 0° C. from 1000° C.	26.0	.0035
Radiation to 0° C. from 500° C.	7.0	.00095
Water quenching	1000–10,000	.1–1.0
Jet turbine blades	35–150	(Cheng. Bradshaw)

Some very complicated shapes will defy all attempts at theoretical treatment and must at present be thermal shock tested on a purely empirical basis.

F. *Heat Transfer Coefficient*

The rate of heating and cooling of a ceramic body obviously affects the performance in thermal shock resisting applications. We have many qualitative examples of variations in heating and cooling rates such as:

Bisque saggers (tunnel kiln cycle, 90 hours).
Titanate setter tile (tunnel kiln cycle, 15 hours).
Chemical porcelain in service.
Spark plugs in service.
Special refractory crucibles in service.
Jet combustion chambers.
Jet turbine blades.

These cases are probably listed in increasing order of severity of thermal shock conditions, but in a most qualitative way. Very little information is available on the quantitative expression of h, the heat transfer coefficient, but the data of Kingery[8] will serve as an orientation to a number of different conditions:

When the temperature differences developed in a thermal shock situation are small, h probably does not vary significantly. When large temperature differences are developed as in jet turbine blades, h probably changes rapidly with temperature. The texture and physical properties of the body under test will, of course, also influence h and the rate of change of h with temperature.

Figure 2 summarizes the present status of several typical ceramic bodies with respect to the maximum quenching temperature which they can withstand under various rates of heat transfer.

REFERENCES FOR CHAPTER VI

8. "Symposium on Thermal Fracture." Jour. Amer. Cer. Soc. 38 (1), January 1955.

9. R. F. Geller, P. J. Yavorsky, B. L. Steierman and A. S. Creamer, "Studies of Binary and Ternary Combinations of Magnesia, Calcia, Baria, Beryllia, Alumina, Thoria and Zirconia in Relation to Their Use as Porcelains." Nat. Bur. Stds. Research Paper 1073, Volume 36, March 1946.

10. F. A. Hummel, "Quenching Vitreous Body Adds Strength," Ceramic Industry Vol. 56, No. 6, 93-94. June 1951.

11. M. D. Karkhanavala, "Bibliography of Thermal Expansion of Glasses." Glass Industry, August, September, October 1952.

12. F. A. Hummel, "Observations on the Thermal Expansion of Crystalline and Glassy Substances." Jour. Amer. Cer. Soc. Vol. 33 (3) 102-107. 1950.

13. G. R. Rigby, "Reversible Thermal Expansion from Theoretical Considerations." Trans. Brit. Cer. Soc. Vol. 50, p. 175-183. 1951.

14. J. B. Austin, "Thermal Expansion of Nonmetallic Crystals," Jour. Amer. Cer. Soc. Vol. 35 (10) 243-253, October 1952.

15. "Thermal Conductivity," Jour. Amer. Cer. Soc. Vol. 37 (2) Part II p. 67-110. February 1954.

CHAPTER VII

THERMAL SHOCK RESISTANCE OF SPECIFIC CERAMICS

F. A. HUMMEL
Pennsylvania State University

Specific Ceramic Bodies

A. High Expansion Group ($a>80$ x 10^{-7})

1. *Magnesia*—The coefficient of expansion of periclase is 140 x 10^{-7} and ware made from MgO therefore is not suitable for severe thermal shock conditions. However, it is widely used for metallurgical crucibles during induction melting where the rate of temperature rise is quite rapid. It need only withstand one cycle of such treatment, however, and it is a rare case when such a crucible can be used a second time. Other uses for MgO are confined to refractory furnace linings and as insulating granules.

2. *Stabilized Zirconia*—The monoclinic-tetragonal volume change which renders pure ZrO_2 rather useless as a thermal shock resisting refractory is well known. The stabilized form of ZrO_2, usually made by adding 5 to 10% of CaO^{16}, does not have the abrupt volume change, but nevertheless the linear coefficient of expansion is quite high, (about 110 x 10^{-7}), and the material does not lend itself to applications where large temperature changes are expected. It is unfortunate that this is the case, since the stabilized material is highly refractory and one of the most chemically inert refractories known.

How Good Is Beryllium Oxide?

3. *Beryllium Oxide*—The exceptionally high thermal conductivity of BeO (See Table IV, Chapter VI) and its good strength was once throught to be sufficient to qualify this oxide as one of great thermal shock resistance, although its linear thermal expansion was in the neighborhood of 88 x 10^{-7}. Extensive testing has shown that a BeO ceramic is not suitable for turbine blades or other similarly severe shocks. It may be chosen for specialized uses in the thermal shock resisting field over other materials of similar expansion characteristics (i.e., corundum) due to its exceptional conductivity which places it above graphite in performance.

4. *Corundum (Al_2O_3), Spinel ($MgAl_2O_4$) and Thoria (ThO_2)*—These compounds are chemically inert and highly refractory (M.P. ThO_2 $3000°$ C.), and the first two are relatively inexpensive, but they qualify as thermal shock resisting materials in only a very limited sense, and again there is close correlation with the linear expansion coefficients, which are between 80-90 x 10^{-7} for all three materials. Corundum is the basis for the aviation spark plug and it is satisfactory for many other less demanding uses such as furnace lining, crucibles and burner parts. Corundum and spinel are

both obtainable in the form of single crystals [17] where the optimum in physical properties is achieved in the materials, yet they cannot be claimed as good thermal shock resisting compounds, even in this highly dense form.

B. *Intermediate Expansion Group* $(20 < a < 80 \times 10^{-7})$

1. *Zircon (ZrSiO$_4$)*—The linear coefficient of expansion of this compound is 40×10^{-7} and it has found several applications as a thermal shock resisting material in the form of crucibles, combustion boats and other laboratory ware.[18] It has some applications in the heavy refractories industry as well.[19] Although it is in general much more highly thermal shock resisting than any of the materials listed in group A, it still does not qualify for use in extreme thermal shock situations. It can be made into very dense or very porous bodies as demanded by the end product.

2. *Mullite (3Al$_2$O$_3$·2SiO$_2$)*—The mullite refractory is best known in the form of bricks, glass tank blocks, protection tubes and chemical laboratory ware. The thermal expansion is in the same range as that of zircon and other properties are quite similar, therefore these two materials have become competitive and interchangeable to a certain extent. A complicating feature in some mullite bodies is the presence of greater or lesser amounts of a glass phase which exerts a very definite influence on the thermal shock resistance.

Properties of Feldspathic Porcelains

3. *Feldspathic Porcelains*—These bodies are representative of the deception which might be experienced if one takes only the coefficient of expansion into consideration and pays no heed to body texture when selecting a thermal shock resisting ceramic body. Porcelains can be made which have relatively low coefficients of expansion, yet they are poor thermal shock resisting bodies due to the large amounts of residual quartz and large amounts of glass phase which are left in the fired body. The combination quartz, glass and mullite presents many opportunities for interfacial or intergranular stress development which leads to failure in thermal shock.

4. *Silicon Carbide (SiC)*—Silicon carbide has proven its value as a thermal shock resisting refractory in the form of setter tile and kiln furniture of many kinds. In addition to its moderately low coefficient of expansion $(a = 35 \times 10^{-7})$, it has a very high thermal conductivity and high strength. One of the most serious disadvantages of SiC is the tending to oxidize to forms of SiO$_2$ which have a most damaging effect on thermal shock resistance. It is usually difficult to obtain the material in dense form, but recent progress has been made[20] in this direction.

5. *Tin Oxide (SnO$_2$)*—Recent data[21] on bodies made from SnO$_2$ indicate high thermal conductivity and relatively low thermal expansion coefficient (37.6×10^{-7}) and the ware appears to be equal to or better than mullite in thermal shock performance. Disadvantages are cost and extreme sensitivity to reducing atmospheres.

6. *Other Compounds*—Some other compounds which might be considered for special purposes are calcium aluminate ($CaO \cdot 2Al_2O_3$, $a = 50 \times 10^{-7}$), anorthite ($CaO \cdot Al_2O_3 \cdot 2SiO_2$, $a = 54 \times 10^{-7}$) and barium aluminum silicate ($BaO \cdot Al_2O_3 \cdot 2SiO_2$, $a = 40 \times 10^{-7}$).

C. *Low Expansion Group* ($a < 20 \times 10^{-7}$)

It is from this group of materials that the best thermal shock resisting performances have been obtained. Until about 1940, the only low expansion materials one had available were fused silica, cordierite and beryl. More recently, aluminum titanate ($Al_2O_3 \cdot TiO_2$), zirconium phosphate ($2ZrO_2 \cdot P_2O_5$), lithium aluminum silicates and the pentavalent oxide group

The General Electric 7077 ceramic triode (left) compared in size to a conventional "peanut" glass envelope tube. Titanium metal parts are sealed to forsterite ceramic parts, using hermetic vacuum seals. This unit is extremely resistant to thermal shock.

Ta_2O_5, Cb_2O_5 and V_2O_5 have been shown to have very low linear thermal expansions when prepared as ceramic aggregates. However, each class of materials appears to have specific disadvantages which place a limitation on its use as a thermal shock resisting ceramic body. The characteristics of each type will be discussed in order.

1. *Fused Silica and Vycor Glass*—These materials have set the standard of thermal shock performance in the glass industry for many years, since they have thermal expansion coefficients in the range $5\text{-}10 \times 10^{-7}$, are isotropic and withstand temperatures up to $1000°$ C. To overcome the limitations of the usual glass forming methods, new processes have been developed which permit the use of slip casting, pressing and extruding of glass powders[22] to give special shapes. It is necessary to reheat the shape made from powdered glass in order to bring about a nonporous condition in the body. Some of the more serious disadvantages of the glasses as thermal shock resisting materials are (1) crystallization at service temperatures in the neighborhood of $1000°$ C., (2) softening under load at elevated temperatures, (3) relatively poor strength, (4) relatively low thermal conductivity.

Cordierite Long Known in Field

2. *Cordierite* $(2MgO \cdot 2Al_2O_5 \cdot 5SiO_2)$—From an historical standpoint cordierite is one of the first, if not the first crystalline thermal shock resisting ceramic material to be discovered. The history of the development of this type of body has been traced by Singer.[23]

Much has been written about ceramic bodies containing cordierite since the discovery in 1925 and the most recent review is by Lamar and Warner.[24] There appears to be some doubt about the exact value of the expansion coefficient of the cordierite crystal, but it is highly likely that it is between 10 to 20×10^{-7}. Bodies based on the cordierite composition, particularly those which have been fired to a dense condition, may develop more or less glass phase as a bond which damages somewhat the thermal shock resisting properties. The compound melts incongruently at $1470°$ C. and to complete liquid at $1530°$ C.

3. *Beryl* $(3BeO \cdot Al_2O_3 \cdot 6SiO_2)$—Beryl has, for many years, been known to be very similar to cordierite in its expansion behavior.[25] It has never developed as an industrial thermal shock resisting material for two reasons. The first is that the commercial material available always contains appreciable alkali impurity which leads to crystalline or glassy phases after firing. These extraneous materials do not permit the basic beryllium aluminum silicate to demonstrate its superior qualities. The second reason for the failure of beryl to appear in the thermal shock picture is that it cannot be prepared by heating pure oxides to high temperatures. The compound can be made by hydrothermal synthesis and it would be interesting to acquire data on the thermal shock performance of large single crystals. Some early data [12] indicate that the directional expansion behavior is quite anisotropic.

A Practical Advance in the Field

4. *Lithium Aluminosilicates*—One of the most recent practical advances in the field of thermal shock resistant ceramics is the β-spodumene or β-spodumene solid solution type of body. The history of this development has been traced by Clark[26] and by Stark and Dilks.[27] The best compositions are those which center around the β-spodumene ratio of $Li_2O \cdot Al_2O_3 \cdot 4SiO_2$, but an entire range of most excellent heat resisting ceramics can be prepared by using spodumene compositions which are either richer or more deficient in silica than the conventional ratio.[28]

As a sidelight in this new field of bodies, a series may be made which contract during heating, thus creating an entirely new type of ware hitherto unavailable to the industry. The success of these contracting bodies depends upon the development of large amounts of β-eucryptite in the fired ware.[29] The materials are finding considerable use in the industry, not always as thermal shock resisting bodies, but in applications where the contracting phenomenon is highly desired, if not indispensable.

Unfortunately, both series of bodies melt at temperatures in the neighborhood of 1400° C., so they cannot be used where high refractoriness is required.

5. *Aluminum Titanate* ($Al_2O_3 \cdot TiO_2$)—The interesting thermal expansion properties of aluminum titanate were first uncovered at the Pennsylvania State University during the thesis work of J. L. Bachman in 1947[30] and fully described in subsequent reports from the university to the Air Material Command, Wright-Patterson Air Force Base, Dayton, Ohio. Later work in other laboratories [31, 32, 33, 34] has extended the knowledge of the thermal and electric behavior of this compound, and the Russians[35] have recently published their results on its unusual thermal expansion properties.

REFERENCES FOR CHAPTER VII

16. Pol Duwez, Francis Odell and F. H. Brown, Jr., "Stabilization of Zirconia with Calcia and Magnesia," Jour. Amer. Cer. Soc. 35 (5) 107-113 (1952).

17. Linde Synthetic Crystals for Industry, Linde Air Products Co., 30 East 42nd St., New York 17, New York.

18. "Zircon Laboratory Ware," Laboratory Equipment Co., St. Joseph, Michigan.

19. "Refractories," Bulletin 202R, The Chas. Taylor Sons Co., Cincinnati, Ohio.

20. "Metal and Self-Bonded Silicon Carbide," WADC Technical Report 54-38 Part II, The New York State College of Ceramics, Alfred University.

21. John Quirk and C. G. Harman, "Properties of a Tin Oxide Base Ceramic Body," Jour. Amer. Cer. Soc. 37 (1) 24-26, 1954.

22. Corning Multiform Glassware Technical Products Division, Corning Glass Works, Corning, New York.

23. F. Singer, "Ceramic Cordierite Bodies," Jour. Can. Cer. Soc. 15, 60-71 (1946).

24. R. S. Lamar and M. F. Warner, "Reaction and Fired-Property Studies of Cordierite Compositions," Jour. Amer. Cer. Soc. 37 (12) p. 602-10, December 1954.

25. Geller, R. F. and Insley, H. I., "Thermal Expansion of Some Silicates of Elements of Group II of the Periodic System," Jour. Research National Bur. Standards 9 (35-46) 1932.

26. John D. Clark, ''Petalite—A New Commercial Mineral,'' Trans. Am. Inst. Mining Met. Engrs. 187 Tech. Pub. No. 2924-H (in Mining Eng. 187, 1068-70, 1950).

27. R. E. Stark and B. H. Dilks, Jr., ''New Lithium Ceramics,'' Metallurgia, 45 (269), 149-50, 1952; Materials and Methods, 35 (1) 98-99, 1952.

28. F. A. Hummel, ''Thermal Expansion Properties of Some Synthetic Lithia Minerals,'' J. Am. Ceram. Soc. 34 (8) 235-39 (1951).

29. F. A. Hummel, ''Significant Aspects of Certain Ternary Compounds and Solid Solutions,'' Jour. Am. Cer. Soc., Vol. 35, No. 3, 64-66 (March 1952).

30. J. L. Bachman, ''Investigations of the Properties of Aluminum Oxide and Some Aluminous Materials,'' M.S. Thesis, Pennsylvania State University, June 1948.

31. Roland Cauville, ''The Electric Properties of the Products of the Oxides of Titanium and Aluminum after Heating Hydrogen,'' Compt. Rend. 229, 1228-30 (1949).

32. M. Hamelin, ''Solid State Reactions of Refractory Oxide Systems Cr_2O_3-MgO-FeO, Al_2O_3-TiO_2, Cr_2O_3-TiO_2 at High Temperatures,'' Rev. Met. 47 324-8 (1950).

33. W. J. Koch and C. G. Harman, ''Aluminum Titanate as a Ceramic Material,'' U. S. Atomic Energy Comm. Tech. Inform. Service, Oak Ridge, Tenn., AECD-3213, 33pp. (1950).

34. S. M. Lang, C. L. Fillmore and L. H. Maxwell, ''The System Beryllia-Alumina-Titania; Phase Relations and General Physical Properties of Three-Component Porcelains.'' Final Report to Office of Naval Research, O.N.R., Project NR 032-074 Contract Na ori 2-47, March 30, 1951.

35. V. A. Bron and A. K. Podnogin, ''Properties of Al_2TiO_5,'' Doklady Akad. Nauk. S.S.S.R. 91, 93-4 (1953).

36. Goro Yamaguchi, ''Studies on Tieilite, Al_2O_3-TiO_2; I,'' J. Japan Ceram. Assoc., 52 (613) 6-7 (1944).

37. G. S. Zhdanov and A. A. Rusakov, ''Isomorphic Series of A_2BO_5 with the Type of Anosovite,'' Doklady Akad. Nauk. S.S.S.R. 82, 901-4 (1952).

38. R. V. Sarakauskas, ''A Study of Compounds Isomorphous With Aluminum Titanate,'' M.S. Thesis, The Pennsylvania State University, June 1952.

39. A. E. Austin and C. M. Schwartz, ''The Crystal Structure of Aluminum Titanate,'' Acta Cryst. 6, 812-13 (1953).

40. G. S. Zhdanov and A. A. Rusakov, ''Rontgenographic Investigation of the Structure of Anosovite and of a New Isomorphous Series of Double Oxides A_2BO_5,'' Trudy Inst. Krist., Akad. Nauk S.S.S.R. 9, 165-210 (1954).

41. Michelle Hamelin, ''Single Crystals of TiO_2-Al_2O_3,'' Compt. rend. 238, 1896-8 (1954).

42. D. E. Harrison, H. A. McKinstry, and F. A. Hummel, ''High-Temperature Zirconium Phosphates,'' Jour. of Amer. Ceram. Soc., Vol. 37, No. 6, June 1954.

43. E. A. Durbin and C. G. Harman, ''An Appraisal of the Sintering Behavior and Thermal Expansion of Some Columbates,'' BMI-791, United States Atomic Energy Commission.

44. B. W. King and L. L. Suber, ''Some Properties of the Oxides of Vanadium and Their Compounds,'' Jour. Amer. Cer. Soc., 38 (9) 306-11, September 1955.

CHAPTER VIII

CERAMIC-TO-METAL SEALS

Leo J. Cronin

Semicon of California, Inc.

The experience on which the material for these articles has been accumulated is based largely on vacuum-tight seals for special electronic tubes called magnetrons.

These tubes and their seals are required to withstand temperatures up to 650° C. during processing and maintain a vacuum on the order of 10^{-6} mm. of Hg during their life. Consequently, reference to seals will be taken to mean high temperature seals using solders with melting points in excess of 700° C. Such solders would include silver, copper, gold and alloys of these metals. Soft solders, silver and platinum paint, and organic bonds are ruled out by this definition.

Limitations of Glass

Glass was used extensively in older magnetrons which operated at lower power and frequency than present magnetrons. The limitations of glass became apparent with the need for higher power, larger and more reliable magnetrons.

Glass could not withstand a 650° C. bakeout, for instance, or survive the passage of high power through a window without melting. Designers of magnetrons, then, were faced with the problem of replacing glass by a more refractory, rugged, low loss material.

In order to see further why glass was inadequate, it may be well to consider the design of specific glass structures. Because the anode operates at ground potential, the cathode must be supported by an insulating structure. In practice, this structure becomes an insulator bushing.

These bushings must withstand the high anode voltage and accompanying electrical stress which leads to corona, arcing or puncture. They must have high insulating value, low loss, and high dielectric strength. In addition to these electrical requirements, the bushings must be physically strong to support the heavy cathode assembly under conditions of rough handling, shock, and vibration.

Other Advantages of Ceramics

Advantages have also been gained in the output window by replacing glass by ceramic. Designers of magnetrons feel that output window assemblies are a necessary evil. They would like a window of zero thickness to eliminate electrical losses, facilitate matching, provide a broadbanded output and avoid vacuum problems.

34

Ceramics down to .009″ thickness have been tested on the mass spectrometer and were tight. They are too thin, however, to provide adequate strength. Experience has placed the useful thickness between 0.060″ and 0.5″ for the majority of seals. Thicker pieces are avoided because of weight, electrical losses, and formation of thermal gradients in processing that lead to cracks.

As a preliminary step, they looked to quartz. At first glance, this looked promising because the electrical losses were low (tan $\delta = .0001 : K_2 = 3.8$ at 10,000 mc/sec) and thermal shock resistance was high.

Drawback to the Use of Quartz

The drawback to the use of quartz is that to make a useful assembly, it has to be sealed to metal in a vacuum tight fashion. This seal has to be not only strong but also must be impervious to gases at temperatures up to about 700° C. for short periods of time (1 hour) and up to 250° C. for its operating life of hundreds and thousands of hours.

Inasmuch as the thermal expansion of quartz does not match that of

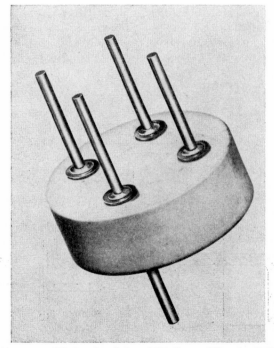

An "area seal" developed by CFI Corp., Mineola, N.Y., gives high reliability to lead-through seals in multiple-terminal as well as single-terminal ceramic-metal composite units.

any metal up to the melting point of hard solder, and is relatively weak mechanically, it is difficult to make practical seals with it.

Looking further, designers examined the properties of other oxides and mica. Mica was eliminated quickly as a material of construction in spite of its desirable electrical properties. From its nature, it is unsuitable, of course, for cylindrical shapes.

Only Possible Use of Mica

The only possible use for mica might be as a flat window. Here again, mica is eliminated—chiefly for these reasons: 1. It is weak mechanically—subject to flaking, disintegration and puncture. 2. It is not practical for large windows of, say, two or three inches in diameter. 3. It will not stand the high temperature bakeout of 600-700° C. 4. It has bonding problems. 5. It is a strategic, expensive material.

Investigating beyond mica and quartz, designers were led to ceramics. Here a wide and confusing selection was available in such bodies as steatites, forsterites, zircons and aluminas. The availability of these ceramics preceded the invention of reliable bonding methods to metal.

Actual sealing practice, then, had to utilize a glass bond between the ceramic and metal. This type of assembly represented an advance but with glass still the limiting material as far as temperatures were concerned. Still, it was possible to effect more power transfer than with a standard

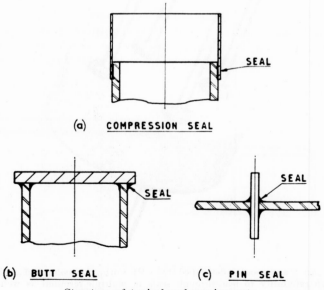

Structure of typical seal requirements.

glass window. Nevertheless, many failures, manifested by leaks or cracks at the glass joint, were encountered.

Without dwelling further on historical details it will suffice to state that numerous combinations of alloys, glasses and ceramics were tried and discarded until the present ceramic-to-metal of Kovar to a high alumina body was standardized.

Basis for Rejection of Materials

Rejection of bodies during the selection of a suitable ceramic was based on various characteristics. Steatites (MgO-SiO_2) and forsterites ($2\ MgO$-SiO_2) have high thermal expansion and relatively low strength, which was enough to eliminate them. In addition, there were problems of narrow maturing range, porosity and nonuniformity.

Until the advent of these high temperature seals, it was impossible to design and operate a magnetron with megawatts of power output. The development of the high alumina ceramic body and a new sealing process allowed, among other advantages, (a) ceramic-to-metal vacuum-tight seals, (b) ceramic output windows transparent to microwave energy and capable of passing high power (10 megawatts or more), (c) close tolerance assemblies, (d) oxide-free assemblies, (e) high temperature processing in hydrogen, (f) multiple simultaneous braze joints, (g) subsequent braze joints closely adjacent, (h) 700° C. exhaust temperatures, (i) reduction in overall magnetron size, (j) more rugged structures and (k) high and low voltage bushings, lead-ins and terminals.

Typical Brazing Process

One good way to follow through a typical brazing practice is to select one of the many seal assemblies and trace its step by step progress. For this purpose, an assembly which we use to evaluate new ceramic bodies

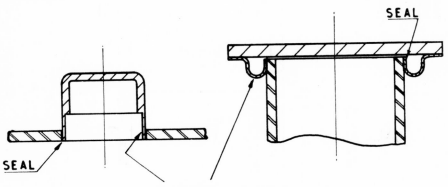

SEAL

SEAL

THIN METAL SECTION

Stress relieved seal arrangements.

has been chosen. This assembly consists simply of a Kovar cylinder (.020-in. wall x 1⅛-in. long x 1⅝-in. O.D.) and a close fitting metallized ceramic disc (⅛-in. thick). They are assembled with one ring of .030-in. copper and sent through a continuous belt conveyor furnace to melt the solder.

After removal from the conveyor furnace, they are checked for vacuum tightness in the helium mass spectrometer leak detector.

It is generally conceded that the Germans performed the early developmental work on ceramic-to-metal seals just prior to World War II. The ceramic body was largely talc with some kaolin, feldspar and zirconium dioxide additions. The metal parts were nickel-iron alloys. Attempts were made to avoid radial tension in seals by having the thermal expansion of the metal greater than that of the ceramic for an outside seal and less than that of the ceramic for an inside or lead-through seal.

The Germans metallized the ceramic by brushing on a layer of fine metal powder paste consisting of 98% Mo and 2% Fe held in an organic binder. This brushing step was followed by a firing at about 1325° C. in a reducing atmosphere, largely hydrogen. A layer of nickel was applied in a similar manner and fired at about 980° C. The purpose of the nickel layer was to facilitate subsequent brazing with hard solder to the assembly.

Early work in this country followed this procedure closely. However, as experience was acquired various American companies developed variations of their own. Today, there are several methods in use throughout the country paralleling the German method closely, differing only in details.

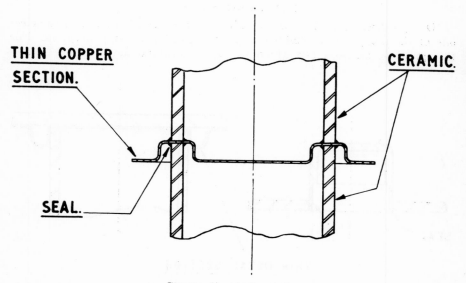

THIN COPPER SECTION.

CERAMIC.

SEAL.

Stress relieved disc seal.

As instances, manganese has been used instead of iron, forsterites have been tried instead of steatites and oxides of molybdenum have been added.

'Active Metals' Method of Sealing

Another general method of sealing is the so-called "active metals" bond. This seal is accomplished by the use of metals such as titanium, zirconium and their hydrides. Because these materials are such excellent getters the formation of their oxides and nitrides must be prevented by making the seal in vacuum or pure hydrogen.

A method typical of this general method is to paint titanium hydride, suspended in a binder, on the ceramic where the braze will be accomplished. Pieces of hard solder are placed over the hydride and melted. The molten solder wets the metal part and the metalized area of the ceramic forming a vacuum-tight brazed joint.

CHAPTER IX

HOW CERAMIC-TO-METAL SEALS ARE MADE

John F. Schuck, Jr.
U. S. Stoneware Co.

As magnetrons were developed for operation at the higher frequency ranges and with higher power output, the glass windows that had been used were no longer satisfactory. Due to the increased frequency, higher dielectric losses were encountered within the glass. This, together with the increased power, caused the glass windows to soften and eventually implode. However, by using a ceramic window in place of the glass assembly, this problem was eliminated.

Higher bake-out temperatures for the magnetrons are an added advantage obtained by the use of ceramic assemblies. The limiting factor for the highest possible bake-out temperature is no longer the softening temperature of the glass but rather the melting temperature of the lowest melting solder used in the tube. As a result bake-out could be accomplished at 700° C. instead of 450° C. This higher temperature makes it possible for shorter exhaust schedules and better vacua.

Increased Mechanical Strength

Even if the above advantages were not present, the increased mechanical strength of the ceramics would be ample reason to warrant their use in place of glass. This ruggedness decreases the scrap due to careless handling and also reduces the possibility of implosion that accompanied the large glass assemblies. Because of the added thermal shock resistance of the ceramic, cracking due to subsequent heating cycles is less apt to be experienced with the ceramic assemblies.

With the trend to miniaturization came the need for small assemblies with high strength and close tolerances. Because the thickness and contour of the glass are difficult to control during the sealing operation, large tolerances are needed. However, by grinding the ceramic very accurately and making the ceramic-to-metal seal as a separate subassembly, close tolerances can be held without difficulty.

Stresses in Ceramic-to-Metal Seals

The strength of the high alumina ceramic used in magnetrons is about 25,000 p.s.i. in tension and 290,000 p.s.i. in compression. As a result of the great differences in these two values, the ceramic-to-metal seal assembly is preferably designed to keep the ceramic either stress-free or in compression. Considering an external seal and neglecting any permanent yield of the metal that might develop during the brazing cycle, the expansion coefficient of the metal will determine the stresses that are produced in the ceramic after the brazing operation. Thus, by using an alloy whose expansion is greater than that of the ceramic (Fig. 1), the desired results of a ceramic in compression can be obtained. It can also be noted that the seal itself is also in compression when such an alloy is used.

Complex Stresses in Internal Seals

Although an alloy with a greater expansion coefficient than the ceramic solves the problem for external seals, internal seals impose more complex stresses. During the cooling of the brazed assembly, both tangential and radial stresses are developed about the inside diameter (I.D.) of the ceramic. The ideal situation, similar to the external seal, would be obtained if both stresses were compressive or if the ceramic were stress-free. However, if a metal has a greater expansion coefficient than the ceramic, tangential cracks may develop during the cooling cycle because the radial stresses are tensile. On the other hand, if a metal such as molybdenum is used, the stresses set up are reversed and radial cracks are apt to result. Of course the diameter of the wire is the determining factor as to whether or not the stresses induce cracking. Whether the coefficient of expansion be larger or smaller than

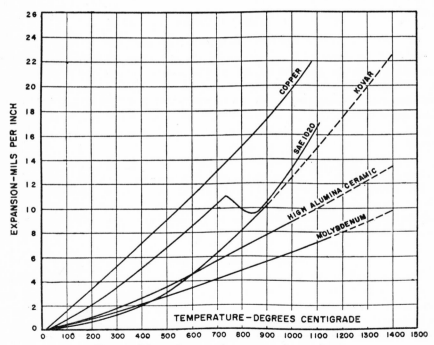

Fig. 1. Thermal expansion curves for various materials used in ceramic-to-metal seals.

the ceramic, small diameter wires of any alloy may be used without causing cracks in the ceramic. However, as the diameter is increased, the stresses also increase and cracking of the ceramic results.

One obvious method to eliminate the above problems would be the use of an alloy that duplicates the expansion curve of the ceramic. This would result in a stress-free assembly. But since such an alloy is not available, design features must be incorporated to make large internal seals possible.

Intermediate Process Necessary

Because of the nature of ceramics, some intermediate process has to be performed on the ceramic before it can be brazed to a metal by standard techniques. The prime process employed in seals to be used in magnetrons is the refractory metal method.

Finely powdered metals, such as Mo-Fe or Mo-Mn, of -325 mesh are applied to the ceramic at the area where the braze is to be made. Although the use of pressed dry powders is being investigated, the usual technique for this application consists of suspending the metal mixture in a suitable nitrocellulose binder and then applying it to the ceramic by means of a brush or spray gun.

Fired in Controlled Hydrogen Atmosphere

This metalized ceramic is fired in a controlled hydrogen atmosphere at a temperature between 1300° C. and 1600° C. The exact temperature of this firing is dictated by the type of metalization as well as the composition and

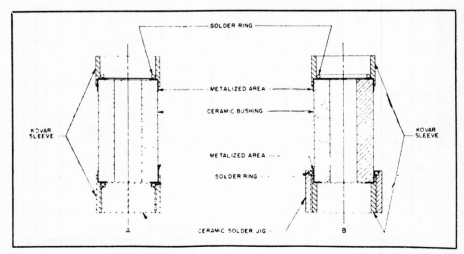

Placement and jigging of solder incorporating the
use of extended metallized areas and ceramic jigs.

firing of the ceramic. During the firing, the metal powders sinter and react with the ceramic to form a strong bond.

However, because of the amount of molybdenum present in the metalized layer, a second coating is needed so that the solder will wet the metalized area of the ceramic during brazing. To fulfill this requirement, a nickel coating can be brushed or sprayed on the initial layer and then fired at about 1000° C. If feasible, a copper or nickel plate can be used in its place. After this second coating the metalized ceramic can be brazed with almost any of the common solders, either hard or soft.

Ceramic-to-Metal Seal Assemblies

Output Windows—Basically, ceramic-to-metal seal assemblies used in magnetrons can be classified into two general categories. The first encompasses those assemblies which are used as output windows in high-power magnetrons, while the second category deals with seals which are primarily insulators.

Of the output windows, the tube-disc window assembly is the simplest and consists of a ceramic disc brazed into a Kovar sleeve. Whenever possible a shoulder is machined on the I.D. of the sleeve to assist in spacing and holding the ceramic during brazing. However, in most cases, to obtain a proper impedance match between the output window assembly and the magnetron, the I.D. must be left free of all protuberances. Thus, with the absence of this shoulder, jigging is necessary to maintain spacing, concentricity and perpendicularity.

Spacing of the disc in the sleeve is controlled by having the ceramic rest upon a metal jig of the necessary length. When an assembly is small in size and there is a possibility of the metal jig brazing to the assembly, a ceramic jig is advisable. A weight is placed on top of the disc to insure against the raising and cooking of the ceramic during the brazing operation.

Gap Between Ceramic and Seal

Due to the greater expansion of the metal, a gap is formed between the ceramic and the sleeve at the brazing temperature. The molten solder, forced by gravity and capillary action, starts to flow into the seal area. However, since the gravitational force overcomes the capillary force, the solder continues down the wall of the sleeve. Thus the seal is deprived of its solder. To prevent this, a tight molybdenum wire ring or ceramic cylinder is placed around the metal to limit the size of the gap at the brazing temperature. Because of the decreased size of the gap, the capillary force will be more apt to retain the solder at the joint.

Instead of utilizing an electrical transition from a rectangular waveguide to a circular waveguide, it is advantageous, in some instances, to use a rectangular seal. Because of the geometry of the seal, appreciable stresses develop in the ceramic and seal. As a result a rectangular seal is not suitable for seals which are to be subjected to subsequent high-temperature brazing operations. However, through careful control a rectangular seal can be a useful feature in magnetron design.

Insulator Assemblies—Of the assemblies that are used for insulation purposes in magnetrons, the bushing assembly is the most prevalent. Although the construction of this assembly is very similar to that of the window assemblies, modifications are made to the basic seal in order to aid the brazing and assembling operations.

To eliminate the rundown of solder without the use of molybdenum wire or a ceramic cylinder, the metalized area of the bushing is extended from the seal area on the outside diameter (O.D.) to part of the flat end of the cylinder. Thus, instead of the molten solder continuing down the sidewall of the sleeve, as was the case in the window assembly, a fillet is formed at the bottom of the seal to keep the solder in the joint. This metalization on the cylinder is also of assistance if it is not possible to place the solder above the seal area. Utilizing a ceramic cylinder as a jig to hold the solder in position, the solder is placed below the seal area but in contact with the metalized end of the cylinder (Fig. 2A). As the solder melts, it wets the metalized surface and by the force of capillary action is drawn up into the joint.

However when this overlap of metalization on the end of the cylinder is used, care must be taken not to metalize too much of the flat surface. If this is done, the seal will be weakened and cracks are apt to develop in the ceramic.

If it is not convenient to place the solder at the underside of the bottom seal, the solder can be placed at the side of the bushing on top of the metalized area (Fig. 2B). The metalization is extended beyond the end of the metal sleeve so that the molten solder will come in contact with the metalization and be forced to flow into the joint rather than down the side of the sleeve.

Flat Seal Also Employed

Another type of seal employed in insulator assemblies is the flat seal. As the name implies, the flat surface of the ceramic is brazed to the flat surface of the metal component. Flat solder stock can be substituted for the rings. But in either case a weight should be placed on the seal in order to keep the assembly concentric and flat. However, if the seal area is of an appreciable size, the stresses due to the expansion difference between the ceramic and metal are of sufficient magnitude to cause severe cracking of the ceramic. Therefore flat seals are carefully investigated before they are used.

Although modifications in seal design, such as the use of a flare or eyelet to hold the solder instead of jigging, or problems due to the shape or size of the ceramic may necessitate minor deviations, the basic principles and steps incorporated above are employed in the majority of the external ceramic-to-metal seal assemblies. Utilizing these principles it has been possible to make a multitude of different assemblies with a minimum of leaky seals.

Internal Seals—As previously mentioned, the stresses that are developed in an internal seal are capable of cracking the ceramic if not controlled. If wires of small diameter, of the order of .080-inch or under, are employed in a seal, the expansion differential between the wire and the ceramic does not cause sufficient stresses to produce cracking. Therefore solid rods are used in most cases. Because molybdenum wires place the seal in compression, it is utilized in the majority of these assemblies. However, it must be kept in mind that although the seal is in compression, tensile stresses are still present in the ceramic.

As the diameter of the wire is increased, the tensile stresses that are set up also increase. This leads to the weakening and cracking of the ceramic. To overcome this, thin-wall Kovar tubing is employed instead of the molybdenum rod. The flexible tubing yields enough to compensate for the expansion difference and in so doing prevents the stresses from developing in the ceramic. Various sizes of coaxial insulators have been made successfully by this method.

Active Metals Technique Utilized

Aside from the standard refractory metal process employed to obtain vacuum-tight ceramic-to-metal seals, the active metals technique is also utilized. This technique is particularly useful in making small I.D. brazes when the standard method of metalizing is not feasible.

Such metals as titanium and zirconium in the form of their hydrides are applied to the ceramic by much the same method as used in the standard process. However there is no need to fire the metalization onto the ceramic in order to obtain a good seal. Instead the part is assembled and then brazed in vacuo or a nonoxidizing atmosphere. During the brazing cycle the hydride dissociates into the pure metal and nascent hydrogen. This active metal in conjunction with the molten solder wets both the ceramic and metal components, and results in a strong vacuum-tight seal.

Because of the affinity these metals have for oxygen, care must be taken to insure that the brazing atmosphere is exceptionally pure. If water vapor or air is present in the system during the brazing operation, an oxide of the metal will form and prevent a vacuum-tight seal.

Use of Titanium Core Solder

A modification of the active metals technique has been the development of titanium-core solder. This solder consists of a silver-copper eutectic wire with a titanium core. Without any previous metalizing of the ceramic, the core solder is placed in position on the assembly to be brazed. As in the case of the hydride, the combination of the pure titanium and molten solder is sufficient to give vacuum-tight seals between the ceramic and metal component. The commercial solder is available with a titanium core of various percentages. In some cases, this percentage is not ample to obtain satisfactory results. To supplement the core, titanium hydride can be applied to the seal to assist in the wetting of the ceramic.

Although this is a 1-shot method for making a ceramic-to-metal seal, an objection to its use is the difficulty in controlling the solder flow. In both the hydride and the titanium cores methods, particles of the titanium are present in the molten solder. Because of this the solder will wet any material with which it comes in contact. Aside from the fact that this makes external jigging difficult, the solder will flow over the ceramic and reduce the insulating surfaces of the assembly. If this is not permissible, wells must be incorporated around the seal area to confine the molten solder within the well diameter. It is also advisable, when using this method, to design the assembly so that it is self-jigging. With all the extra design features that must be incorporated in this type of seal, it is usually more economical to use the standard refractory metal process.

Evaluation Tests Needed

Because the firing temperature, firing cycle, composition and other variables in the manufacture of ceramics have a major effect on the strength of a ceramic-to-metal seal, evaluation tests are needed to insure receipt of ceramics with proper sealing properties. Therefore, all ceramics that are to be treated with the standard high-temperature metalization and used in vacuum-tight seals must pass two evaluation tests before acceptance.

The first test is used to determine the ability of the ceramic to maintain a vacuum-tight seal under pressure. This is accomplished in the following manner.

Eight to 10 green discs (1/8-inch thick) are included in each kiln firing which contains ceramics to be used in seals. After being fired each disc is metalized and brazed into a Kovar sleeve (.020-inch wall x 1 1/8 inches long x 1 5/8 inches O.D.) with one ring of .030 copper solder. Each assembly is then vacuum-tested by a helium mass spectrometer leak detector. If the assembly is vacuum-tight it is subjected to a pressure of 1600 pounds by means of a dynamometer.

This pressure is applied to the seal by means of two steel plugs each fitted at one end with a rubber disc. With these discs toward the ceramic, the plugs are inserted into the Kovar sleeve. This entire assembly is then placed in the dynamometer and pressure applied to the exposed ends of the steel plugs. As the pressure is increased, the rubber discs are compressed and forced against the Kovar wall just above and below the seal area. As the Kovar is forced to bulge by the compressed rubber discs, an increasing stress is developed in the seal. The pressure on the plugs, and thus on the seal, is increased until eventually a leak develops.

Apply Pressure in Leak Tests

In order to determine and correlate the amount of pressure necessary to produce a leak in these test seals, the pressure, after the initial value of

1600 pounds, is increased in increments of 200 pounds. The assembly is leak-tested after each increment until a leak is produced. The pressure that caused the leak is then recorded. All values for the one kiln firing are then averaged and the resultant value assigned to that particular firing. If this average does not meet the minimum acceptable test value, which has been determined by past testing, the entire kiln firing is rejected. As an added control and precaution against faulty metalization or firing, a stand-ard ceramic which is known to be of an acceptable firing is also sent through the test with the firing samples.

The second acceptance test was incorporated because the majority of ceramic-to-metal seals employed in magnetrons have to withstand a number of subsequent heat cycles during the assembly of the magnetron.

Bond Test Performed on Ceramics

To decrease further the possibility of obtaining faulty ceramics and ex-periencing leakers in the assembly of magnetrons, a bond test is performed on all ceramics before they are employed in tubes. The bond test is per-formed on six sample ceramics that are taken at random from each type of ceramic part to be used in vacuum seals. If more than one firing is in-volved for each type, six test ceramics are selected from each firing. These samples are then brazed into the subassemblies for which they were ordered. All vacuum-tight seals are then sent through a continuous belt conveyor furnace which is operated at 800° C. If the assemblies remain vacuum-tight after six passes through this furnace, the remaining parts of the order are accepted. However if sample parts not not pass the test the ceramics are rejected. The six passes are an arbitrary limit. Some seals have passed through this test over 25 times without failing.

The bond test is also useful in the evaluation of a newly designed seal. If a seal has the strength to withstand the stresses that develop in it during the six passes through the furnace, the seal is usually strong enough to remain vacuum-tight during the subsequent brazing and bake-out operations of a magnetron.

Life Tests Often Used

However, life tests are often incorporated in the testing of a new design technique. This is accomplished by attaching an ionization gauge to the seal and then evacuating and sealing off the assembly.

The gas ionization current flowing through the gauges is measured peri-odically and gives a measure of the vacuum. An increase in the current through the gauge indicates that a leak has developed in the assembly.

CHAPTER X

ALUMINA BODIES FOR CERAMIC-TO-METAL SEALS

F. J. HYNES

Raytheon Mfg. Co.

The previous two chapters in this series have described some general characteristics of good seals and how to obtain them. One of the most basic fundamentals is a reproducible ceramic body. Some requirements for a ceramic body for use in ceramic-to-metal sealing are:

1. Vacuum tightness.
2. Good thermal shock resistance.
3. Good mechanical properties.
4. Good electrical properties.
5. High softening temperature.
6. Economical fabrication.
7. Uniformity, from lot to lot, in the above-mentioned characteristics.

As explained in Chapter VIII, a high alumina body was chosen because of all ceramic bodies it most nearly meets the above requirements.

Little Trouble with Vacuum Tightness

Vacuum tightness—Little trouble has been encountered with this. Many commercial alumina and laboratory research bodies have been ground to .010 inches thick and found to be impervious to helium gas on the mass spectrograph. This is well below minimum thickness in most cases.

Good thermal shock resistance—Thermal shock resistance characteristics are difficult to define unless definite conditions are stated. Generally, however, in sealing practice thermal shock failure results from too rapid heating. In this respect alumina bodies have proved better than forsterites or steatites.

Good mechanical strength is one of the desirable features of alumina bodies. Its flexural and impact strength are about twice as good as those of a steatite body. This is of particular advantage in magnetron tubes where large windows (3 to 4 inches in diameter) are exposed to mechanical abuse. High strength is also necessary to withstand stresses involved in sealing practices. Table 1 gives a tabulation of some mechanical properties of a typical high alumina (90-95%) body. As these values are a composite, a particular body may have higher values than those listed. Depending on the fluxing materials, method of processing in manufacture and the nature of processing in the refractory metal process, these mechanical properties will also vary in the ceramic when it is in a completed ceramic-to-metal seal assembly.

Good Electrical Properties Desired

Good electrical properties—Good alumina bodies are Grade L-5 under JAN-1-10 Insulating Materials, Ceramic Radio, Class L specifications. They may be expected to have characteristics similar to values depicted in Fig. 1 in regard to dielectric constant and loss tangent; moreover, these good characteristics are maintained to a large extent as the temperature is increased. This is particularly advantageous when dealing with high energy transfer structures as in magnetrons or when equipment is subjected to the higher ambient temperatures required in modern electronic practice.

High softening temperature—It is obvious when using the refractory metal process that no distortion, warping or blistering should occur when the first coating is fired on. Most 90-95% alumina bodies have softening points in excess of 1600° C. and thus are safe in this respect.

Economical fabrication—As compared to forsterite, zircon porcelain and steatite bodies, the common insulating materials used for ceramic-to-metal seals, aluminum oxide porcelains are more expensive. Chapter VIII explains how other conventional bodies were tried and found lacking in

TABLE I

Typical properties of high alumina body

Specific Gravity	3.6
Softening Temperature	1700° C.
Therm. Exp. Co. 25-1000° C.	9.14×10^{-6}
Compressive Strength	200,000 psi
Modulus of Rupture	45,000 psi
Tensile Strength	25,000 psi
Impact Resistance	35 inch lbs/in^2
Dielectric Strength	300 volts
T$_e$ Value	950° C.
Surface Finish (80-grit wheel)	75 microinches

one or more technical requirements. When one considers the cost of magnetron tubes and the fact that the insulators cost considerably less than 1% of the total value, the differences are insignificant. When used in other vacuum-tight structures or mechanical assemblies where high strength and good thermal shock properties are paramount, ruggedness and reliability are generally the criteria used in the selection of an insulating material.

Uniformity—Alumina bodies have a characteristically long firing range and thus the chemical, mechanical and electrical properties can be controlled to desired limits.

Types of Alumina Available

Raw Materials—Adequate supplies of Bayer process alumina are available to the ceramic manufacturer. In general there are two types of alumina suitable to manufacture high alumina bodies—calcined and fused.

Commercial bauxite, from which the high grade alpha-alumina is derived, is composed of gibbsite ($Al_2O_3 \cdot 3 H_2O$) and diaspore ($Al_2O_3 \cdot H_2O$). This ray material is rendered free of chemical impurities by the Bayer process and calcined in shaft kilns or fused in electric furnaces.

Whether calcined or fused grades are used, it is important to remember that Bayer process alumina contain small amounts of soda. Alkalis should be kept to a minimum to avoid

1. Nonuniformity in the ware due to volatilization.
2. Low strength characteristics and
3. Higher dielectric losses.

Calcined grades normally contain over 95% alpha-alumina because in heating to temperatures of at least 1100° C. in suitable atmospheres, the water molecules are removed and the mass is converted to hexagonal alpha-alumina. There may be other phases such as sodium-beta-alumina ($1 Na_2O \cdot 11 Al_2O_3$) or anhydrous grades, depending on the chemical impurities present and the conditions of the calciner.

Ceramic properties such as ease of grinding, shrinkage and reactivity are affected by the different calcined and fused aluminas. Shrinkage of calcined alumina is greater than fused alumina in pressed ware.

Some Bodies Need High Temp Firing

When firing bodies containing 10-15% of fluxes, higher temperatures are needed because of the reduced activity of the fused alumina. Thus in practice the use of one or more grades of calcined alumina or of fused and calcined alumina may be advantageous.

Other impurities normally contained in alumina are iron oxide, titanium dioxide and silica. Iron oxide of course adversely affects the electrical properties and titanium dioxide will cause blackening of the ceramic ware in later processing. As little as .25% TiO_2 will turn the ceramic black when exposed to the temperatures and atmospheres used in the refractory metal process. Thus these two impurities should be kept to a minimum.

Typical analyses of high alumina bodies show various amounts of silica. The silica in the alumina should be low but, more important, it should be uniform from batch to batch so as not to upset the balance between alumina and the other fluxing materials.

Variety of Materials Added

Review of the existing literature, particularly that pertaining to spark plugs, indicates that a great variety of materials have been added with alumina in body formulation. Some of these are materials of the sillimanite group, various kinds of clay, talcs and other silica bearing minerals, alkaline earth oxides, phosphates, oxides of chromium, zirconium, titanium and a host of other metallic oxides.

Ceramic-to-metal seal bodies generally may be classed as glass-bonded alumina bodies. Thus added to the silica are sufficient alkaline earth materials to give a viscous glass phase. In addition, materials may be added to control grain growth.

Body Preparation—Alumina bodies are usually ball-milled with HCl as a deflocculant to a fine average particle size (2-10 microns). The mill linings and balls consists of a high-alumina composition, preferably of the same composition as the body. Thus no correction factor for increased amounts of silica is needed. Rubber linings can also be used.

Liberal use of magnetic separators, both dry and wet, must be made to remove the last traces of iron. Iron particles contained in a magnetron window will cause localized hot spots due to higher electrical losses leading to failure of the window from thermal shock or loss of vacuum.

Processing steps after ball milling are conventional and are dictated by the method of forming.

Four Forming Methods Used

Forming Methods—There are four commonly used methods of forming alumina shapes. Pressing is by far the most commonly used method. By the use of a spray dryer, a free flowing granular powder can be obtained which is very satisfactory for automatic tablet pressing. Parts such as magnetron windows and spacers can easily be pressed this way.

When pressing cylinders of relatively long length, hydrostatic pressing must be resorted to because density differentials set up by the two moving punches cause a "Mae West" fired shape. This method, which can be

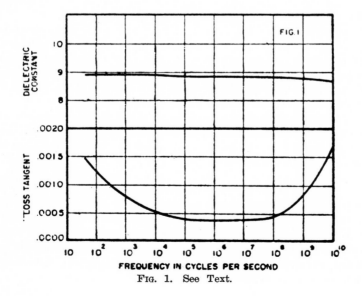

FIG. 1. See Text.

highly mechanized, is particularly advantageous in that uniform density is accomplished in the piece. This leads to uniformity and reproducibility of fired dimensions and physical properties. One surface, usually the outside, must be machined after pressing; this is accomplished by a diamond tool or an abrasive wheel. Coaxial magnetron output windows can be made ideally in this manner.

Many types of tubing, both thin and thick-rolled, can be extruded. Care must be exercised in the die and pin design and in the proper extrusion binders so that laminations do not occur. In subsequent firing of the refractory metal coating, these laminations can open up. Leaks have been traced in faulty insulators along the extruded axis. Where hydrostatic pressing facilities are lacking, the extrusion method can be used to supply blanks for turning.

Nonuniform Shapes by Casting

Nonuniform cross sectional shapes can be made by casting. Good dense pieces can be obtained with casting but mold wear is greater than when casting a conventional whiteware body. Extreme care must be taken to avoid air entrapment as wall thicknesses increase.

A method for forming complicated shapes finding increasing use in injection or compression molding. Nearly any shape can be made by mixing ceramic and plastic materials and forming under heat and pressure. Molding dies are expensive and are subject to short lives due to the abrasive action of the alumina. Moreover, removal of the carbonaceous material requires special ovens or slower kiln cycles. In spite of these technical difficulties, a great many complicated electronic parts are made in this manner.

Firing—The firing of alumina seal bodies, as in the case of all electrical bodies, is one of the most important stages of manufacture. Firing is generally carried out in tunnel kilns. Modern kiln practice has dictated relatively small kilns with a setting space of approximately 9 to 20 ins. wide x 1 to 2 ft. high with a length of about 100 ft.

Reasons for Using Small Kilns

There are many reasons for this type of kiln, some of which are:

1. Refractory problems associated with the arch in the high-temperature section.

2. Ware dimensions.

3. General economics
   a) Initial installation charge. The cost of the super refractory brick is a large item here.
   b) Capacity demands.
   c) Ratio of large ware to small ware. This ratio is usually small.

Whether a periodic or tunnel kiln, it is economically desirable to use the products of combustion to heat the ware or the secondary air.

Grinding—One additional processing step, not normally required in whiteware production, is finish grinding as stated in Chapter IX; dimensional control of the ceramic, metal layer and Kovar sleeves must be maintained. This generally means the ceramic piece must be held to $\pm.001$ in the sealing area. Special designs might warrant closer tolerances or other alignment features. Accuracy of the fired specifications is difficult to hold closer than $\pm.5\%$ of the shrinkage factor for the part; thus as the parts increase in size and complexity the chances of holding the sealing tolerance diminish. When one considers the need for roundness, concentricity and perpendicularity of the surfaces, the need for diamond grinding became obvious. A close scrutiny of the ceramic-to-metal seal design must be made with respect to the ceramic piece because often this is the most expensive and difficult-to-obtain item in the assembly.

Two Possible Grinding Methods

Discs are normally used as magnetron windows. The grinding operation depends on the method of manufacture. Two possibilities are suggested:

1. Blanks can be hydrostatically pressed or extruded. The fired blanks can be centerless-ground and then cut off to length by a diamond wheel.

2. Window shapes can be pressed on a tablet machine. Both surfaces of the windows can be ground on a surface grinder. Ground windows can be stacked together and the diameter ground on an O.D. grinder.

Cylinders are normally used for voltage bushings, lead-ins and terminals. These may be made by using the forming methods described above. The outside surface may be conveniently centerless-ground or jigged on the I.D. and ground on the O.D. In large bushings where outside surface area is large compared to the metalizing area, the seal area may be conveniently plunge-ground. In the normal bushing the inside surface need not be ground. It is important to remember that the proper surfaces must be perpendicular where jigging is involved. Thus, in the window assembly, electrical requirements demand that the faces be parallel and the metalized area be perpendicular to the faces (see Chapter IX).

Internal grinding is to be avoided wherever possible because it is more costly than the other two types of grinding. For internal seals of diameters on the order of .080 inches, no problem is encountered in sealing because the necessary dimensions can be held as the part. As the inside diameter increases, the necessity for diamond grinding increases. The part should be so designed that if the part is long only a minor percentage of the inside diameter need be ground. When internal seals are to be made, consideration should be given to the use of ultrasonic methods to drill the entire hole in the case of short pieces or to remove stock in the I.D. in longer pieces.

Checking the Alumina Body

Most manufacturers of alumina bodies have process controls that are used at such points as mixing, grinding, forming and firing. We would like to call attention to some measures that can be used to check the suitability of an alumina body for ceramic-to-metal seals.

Visual Observations—It is quite obvious that each lot of insulators should be given a physical check for defective pieces. Pieces should be rejected if they have cracks, chips or holes, or contain evidences of foreign material. Dimensional tolerances can also be measured at this time.

Specific Gravity—This simple nondestructive test can be easily run on every shipment of insulators received. By using accurate balances and normal care, a reproducibility of ±.005 gms/cc can be obtained in specific gravity determinations. A closely controlled body will be in the limits of ±.02 gms/cc. Abnormal fluctuation will indicate overfiring or underfiring or possibly the presence of closed pores from a deceptive forming.

Modulus of Rupture—By using a piece (1½″ dia. x ⅛″ thick) as described in Chapter IX of this book, strength measurements can be performed. Close correlation exists between modulus of rupture and specific gravity. Thus, after sufficient data are accumulated, an estimate of strength can be obtained nondestructively by using the specific gravity as a guide. It is well, however, to consider the continued use of the modulus of rupture test, particularly when using the refractory-metal process. Here again, not only overfiring or underfiring of the body but also changes due to variations of the hydrogen firing can be detected.

Reflected Light Microscopy

Polished Sections—Reflected light microscopy will reveal the typical structure of the body in question. It is not practical to use photomicrography extensively as a control tool but it is well to know the appearance of the microstructure.

Bond Checks—A bond test should be included in any quality control program. Chapter IX clearly outlines two types of effective bond tests. After the initial hydrogen firing in the refractory metal process, the ceramic pieces should be checked for changes in physical dimensions, blistering, metallic inclusions or slumping of any kind.

CHAPTER XI

THE NATURE AND USES OF FERROELECTRICITY

LAWRENCE BICKFORD
International Business Machines Corp.

GILBERT GOODMAN
General Electric Co.

Author's Note

Over the past several years there has been a great deal of confusion concerning the terminology and classification of ferroelectric materials.

Barium titanate crystallizes in the simple perovskite structure (Fig. 1), a most accommodating structure which tolerates a copious amount of ionic substitution. Thanks to this fortunate circumstance, the physical and chemical properties can be varied over a wide range.

Barium titanate and its substitutes have such interesting dielectric properties that they were hailed as a new type of dielectric material and accorded a special classification by themselves: Titanate dielectrics. Their interesting piezoelectric properties qualified them as charter member in the field of ceramic transducers.

It has been overlooked or unrecognized that these special properties are either the direct result of or owe their significance in ceramic bodies to the fact that the titanates are ferroelectric.

The confusion regarding terminology results because many descriptive terms were transplanted bodily from the field of ferromagnetics.

One of the primary objectives of this article is to clear up some of the confusion alluded to. In order to do this we shall attempt to explain what ferroelectricity is and why it is so useful a property. It should be pointed out that there is much about the subject which is not yet understood and that a great deal of research work, both theoretical and experimental, is currently being carried out in this fascinating field.

All matter is electrical in nature, containing both positive and negative charges. In ionic structures, which we shall use for our descriptive model, the positive charge is identified with the cation, and the negative charge with the anion. The material is normally electrically neutral and unpolarized. By this we mean that the quantity of positive charge equals the quantity of negative charge and the electrical center of gravity of the positive charge coincides in space with that of the negative charge.

Now let us make a capacitor out of our piece of material by applying metal electrodes to two opposite surfaces. A capacitor can be regarded as a device for storing electrical charge.

If we connect the capacitor plates to a battery, free charge flows from the battery to the capacitor plates until the potential drop across the capacitor equals the battery voltage. The amount of free charge required depends upon the polarizability of the material inside the capacitor. The accumulation of free charge on the capacitor plates creates an electric field within the material which attracts the cations toward the cathode and the anions toward the anode.

Ionic Response to Forces

Polarizability is a measure of the amount of ionic response to these forces, and is determined by how strongly the ions are held in their equilibrium positions. Any resulting ionic displacement tends to reduce the electric field inside the material.

More free charge must flow from the battery to the capacitor electrodes to restore the electric field to the equilibrium value determined by the battery voltage and physical dimensions of the capacitor. When equilibrium is attained, the material is polarized: the centers of gravity of positive and negative charge no longer coincide.

The material parameter describing its polarizability is the dielectric constant, usually denoted by K. The capacitance of a capacitor is defined as the quantity of free charge on either plate per volt of potential difference between the plates.

Obviously, materials of high dielectric constant are desirable since they permit the fabrication of capacitors with large capacitance but small physical dimensions.

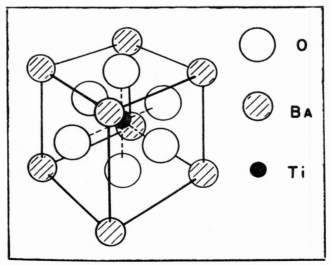

FIG. 1. The structure of barium titanate. Displacement of positively charged titanium with respect to its surrounding negatively charged oxygen environment is thought to be largely responsible for the polarization and hence the ferroelectricity of barium titanate.

So far we have seen that a material has a large dielectric constant if it is highly polarizable; that is, if the cations and anions are displaced a relatively large distance in opposite directions under the influence of an applied electric field.

It was implied, but not directly stated, that a polarized dielectric will have bound charges on those surfaces which face the electrodes. This bound charge exists because ionic displacement has resulted in a slight net excess of negative charge in the surface layers of the dielectric adjacent to the anode, and of positive charge adjacent to the cathode. The bound charge density is directly proportional to the polarization.

Ions Return to Equilibrium

When the electric field is removed, the ions return to their equilibrium positions. In normal dielectrics this condition corresponds to a state with no bound surface charge and no polarization. The centers of gravity of positive and negative charges once again coincide in space.

There exists a large group of materials in which some degree of polarization persists. Ferroelectric materials belong to this class. They are not its sole members, however, for the possession of a spontaneous polarization is only one of the requisites for membership in the class of ferroelectrics.

When a spontaneous polarization exists, a crystal in its equilibrium condition cannot have a center of symmetry, since the charge centers of gravity do not coincide. A physical deformation of such a crystal will change the ionic separation and therefore change the magnitude of its polarization.

Conversely, any electrically induced change in polarization will result in a mechanical deformation of the crystal. This electrical-elastic interaction is called piezoelectricity. It is utilized in devices known as transducers, which convert mechanical energy into electrical energy, and vice versa.

Materials with Bound Surface Charge

Materials which possess a spontaneous polarization must as a consequence have a bound surface charge. Usually this charge cannot be detected because it has been neutralized over a long period of time by charges absorbed from the surrounding atmosphere. When the temperature changes the polarization also changes and a surface charge can be detected. This charge apparently induced by heat is called pyroelectricity.

Quartz is pyroelectric and piezoelectric, but it is not ferroelectric. One requirement not yet described must be satisfied before a material can be classified as ferroelectric: the direction of its polarization must be controllable by a relatively weak applied electric field. The control mechanism is the formation and propagation of domain walls, which are boundaries separating microscopic regions called domains.

Within each domain the polarization has a given orientation, either north or south, parallel to the crystallographic axes. If the volume of domains oriented north is equal to that of domains oriented south, the sample will have no net polarization although the spontaneous polarization persists within each domain. This domain structure is directly analogous to the magnetic domain structure existing in ferromagnetic materials. Since energy is dissipated during domain wall propagation the material is characterized by a hysteresis loop.

Polarization Destroyed by Heat

The spontaneous polarization is destroyed by heat. The temperature at which it disappears is called the Curie temperature, a term which was adopted from the corresponding magnetic phenomenon. The dielectric constant becomes very large in the vicinity of the Curie temperature, as is shown in Figure 2. It is this large magnitude and strong temperature dependence of the dielectric constant of titanates and related materials which makes them technologically useful. Some attempts have been made by admixture to retain the large value of dielectric constant but make it invariant with respect to temperature. The fact that the high value is associated with the Curie temperature makes such a goal impractical.

Finally, the onset of spontaneous polarization at the Curie temperature accompanies a small crystallographic transformation. Barium titanate becomes tetragonal in its ferroelectric state. One of the cubic axes of the

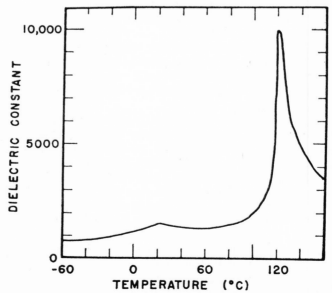

FIG. 2. Dielectric constant of barium titanate as a function of temperature. The peak at 120° C., the Curie temperature, is associated with the onset of ferroelectricity.

high temperature modification becomes the tetragonal axis, which is the direction of alignment of the polarization.

Ceramic barium titanate can be partially oriented by applying an electric field as it cools through the Curie temperature. That cubic direction of each crystallite most nearly parallel to the field direction becomes the tetragonal axis and therefore some degree of alignment between crystallites is obtained.

A ceramic thus takes on some of the characteristics of a single crystal. The usefulness of ceramic barium titanate as a transducer stems from this effect.

What Materials May Be Ferroelectrics

Keeping in mind the criteria just discussed, let us consider what materials may possibly be ferroelectrics and in which of these the characteristics have actually been observed and used.

In the technical literature, it is possible to find information on the crystallographic properties of thousands of chemical compounds. It is possible to pick out those which lack a center of crystallographic symmetry and which possess a permanent polarization.

In doing this, one will have selected a very large number of materials which possess one of the requisite properties of a ferroelectric. It remains to apply a second test to determine whether the permanent polarization can be reversed in direction by some attainable electric field.

In practice a number of problems would be associated with this search procedure. First of all, the initial selection operation would supply a tremendous number of dipole-containing materials for further test. Secondly, although the published data may indicate that a permanent polarization is present, its magnitude may be so small as to make it either difficult or impossible to measure. In such a case, ascertaining its reversibility would be equally difficult if not impossible.

A very similar situation was encountered in the feverish search for new non-strategic piezoelectric crystals during World War II. Large numbers of natural and synthetic materials were examined which were known from x-ray data to properly lack structural symmetry. In other words, every material examined was known in advance to be piezoelectric. However, only a small percentage gave a positive test for piezoelectricity, and in only a few of these was the effect large enough to be useful.

Eliminating Possible Materials

Suppose that as a result of the first stage of our large scale exploration for new and unheard of ferroelectrics a number of materials posssesing large permanent polarizations was at hand. Application of the next criterion—the reversibility of the polarization by an electric field—would probably again weed out a very high percentage of these.

Possibly some of the materials could be shown to be ferroelectric by use of a sufficiently high field strength, but the practical limitation on attainable voltage would cause them to be eliminated as possibilities.

In view of these unfavorable factors tending to limit the discovery of new ferroelectric materials, it would seem that sheer luck has played an important part in our present knowledge of them. For example, the fact that titania and magnesium titanate made desirable capacitor materials led to work with barium titanate and to subsequent discovery of its unusual properties.

The general trend has been to discover ferroelectricity in materials related to the original barium titanate and Rochelle salt. More outlying areas have yet to yield any results, probably because of the difficulties enumerated above.

CHAPTER XII

FERROELECTRIC CERAMICS

LAWRENCE BICKFORD
International Business Machines Corp.

GILBERT GOODMAN
General Electric Co.

The engineer charged with synthesizing ceramics for specialized electrical use can choose the components of his bodies from a large variety of interesting materials. The newest and perhaps the most useful additions to his raw materials warehouse are the ferroelectrics.

Actually the existence of ferroelectrics as a class of materials has been known for a long time. However, the early ferroelectrics were merely of academic interest so far as the ceramic engineer was concerned, for they were hydrated salts which could not be utilized in ceramic bodies.

This situation was changed during the late war. Out of the cauldron of wartime research emerged a new type of ferroelectric with barium titanate, a simple refractory oxide, as its prototype. The piezoelectric and unique dielectric properties of barium titanate are either the direct result of or owe their significance in ceramic bodies to the fact that the titanates are ferroelectric.

Ferroelectrics do not in general contain iron, as one might imagine from the name. They merely have properties which can be regarded as the electrical analog of the ferromagnetic properties of iron.

Ferroelectric Properties

To be ferroelectric a material must be inherently polarizable and the direction of its polarization must be controllable by a relatively weak applied electric field.

When spontaneous polarization exists, any physical deformation of a crystal of the material will cause a change in the magnitude of polarization. Conversely, any electrically induced change in polarization will result in a mechanical deformation of the crystal. This electrical-elastic interaction is called *piezoelectricity*. It is utilized in devices known as transducers which convert mechanical energy into electrical energy, and vice versa.

Because of the nature of the subject and the confusion in terminology that exists, an explanation of what ferroelectricity is and why it is so useful a property is in order. A simple and yet rather complete explanation, prepared especially for the reader who is not too familiar with ferroelectricity or with electronics, can be found in Chapter XI.

Ferroelectric Materials

Table 1 lists the oxide compounds presently known to be or suspected of being ferroelectric. The suspects are marked with an asterisk.

The materials included in Table 1 are sufficiently varied that it would be unfeasible to give a detailed account of the ceramic processing of each one, even if this information were available. In many cases, the fabrication techniques have been investigated only sufficiently to yield specimens for dielectric testing. Therefore, the following paragraphs will deal in a general way with the ceramic difficulties common to many of the oxides, but specifically with the processing of only one.

TABLE I

Formula	Name	Curie temperature	Room temperature symmetry and structure	Ref.
		° C.		
$BaTiO_3$	Barium titanate	120	tetragonal, perovskite	
$PbTiO_3$	Lead titanate	490	tetragonal, perovskite	(1)
$CdTiO_3$	Cadmium titanate	approx. −220	ilmenite	(2, 3)
$SrTiO_3$	Strontium titanate*	approx. −263	perovskite	(4)
$(Pb, Ba)ZrO_3$	Modified lead zirconate			(5, 6)
$(Pb, Ba)SnO_3$	Modified lead stannate*	150		(7)
$NaVaO_3$	Sodium vanadate	approx. 330	perovskite (?)	(8)
$NaNbO_3$	Sodium niobate*	360	orthorhombic, perovskite	(10)
$LiNbO_3$	Lithium niobate	?	ilmenite	(9)
$KNbO_3$	Potassium niobate	420	orthorhombic, perovskite	(11)
$PbNb_2O_6$	Lead niobate	570	orthorhombic	(12)
$Cd_2Nb_2O_7$	Cadmium niobate	−103	pyrochlore	(13)
$LiTaO_3$	Lithium tantalate	> 350	ilmenite	(9)
$NaTaO_3$	Sodium tantalate	approx. 475	ilmenite	(14)
$KTaO_3$	Potassium tantalate	−260	ilmenite	(15)
$RbTaO_3$	Rubidium tantalate	approx. 245		(16)
$PbTa_2O_6$	Lead tantalate*	260		(7)
MoO_3	Molybdic oxide*	> 530 (?)	anatase	(16)
WO_3	Tungstic oxide	approx. 750 (?)	rhenium oxide	(17)

Problems with Raw Materials

Raw materials—The first practical problem in making one of the ferro-electrics of Table 1 has to do with raw materials. Barium titanate is well established today and can be bought in powder form for ceramic use.

If, however, one wished to make lead tantalate ceramics, it would be necessary to use lead and tantalum oxides, or compounds which would yield these oxides, and react them with one another to form the tantalate. This would necessitate mixing, heat treatment and crushing operations which are carried out by the material supplier in the case of barium titanate.

To date, unfortunately for the ceramist, no clay or similar colloidal mineral has been found to be ferroelectric. Such a discovery would be a happy one because the known ferroelectrics have notoriously poor ceramic forming qualities.

Plasticity, suspensibility and dry strength common to clays are basically lacking in these materials but can be imparted to a limited extent through fine grinding and the use of organic additives. Such a procedure is general practice in forming ferroelectric ceramics.

Have Narrow Firing Range

Another problem has to do with the narrow firing range of these materials. In using the oxide ferroelectrics, one is generally capitalizing on the peculiarities of a particular chemical compound.

Any fluxes, glasses or other foreign matter added to improve working properties tend to modify, dilute or even destroy the desirable properties. Yet the pure material, a chemical compound, is likely to have a sharp melting point and firing treatments at a lower temperature generally yield a porous ceramic. Note the difference between this situation and that of the average ceramic formulation with multiple constituents whose properties can be manipulated to give an easily-handled material.

Chemical Reduction—Examination of Table 1 discloses that almost every compound listed contains one or more atoms capable of existing in lower valence states than those they occupy in the ferroelectric. Thus, barium titanate contains Ti^{4+} which could also exist as Ti^{3+}. In other words, there is the possibility of chemical reduction of the ferroelectric compound.

In the reduced condition, the desirable properties are either lost or blanketed by new undesirable properties. This condition can arise from injudicious use of a reducing atmosphere or too high temperatures during the firing operation. Yet it has recently been found in the case of barium titanate that firing conditions capable of reducing the compound can, when properly controlled, yield ceramics of much higher density than before. The use of various nonoxidizing furnace atmospheres for at least a portion of the firing cycle to produce high quality barium titanate ceramics has been reported.[18]

Volatility of Constituents—Another type of instability frequently encountered is due to volatility of one of the oxide constituents: lead oxide in lead zirconate, for example. On a small scale this tendency has been overcome by sealed firing in an atmosphere rich in PbO. This technique has not been employed on a larger than laboratory scale.

Fabrication of Ferroelectrics

The fabrication of barium titanate has been described in detail in a previous article by Ruffner. Let us discuss the procedures used with potassium niobate, one of the newer materials, as described in the patent literature. First, crystals of the compound are prepared by melting at 1200° C. the following mixture:

2.6 weight parts K_2SO_4
1.55 weight parts K_2CO_3
3.00 weight parts Nb_2O_5

The melt is cooled to 700° C. at about 15° C. per hour, then cooled rapidly to room temperature. The resulting ferroelectric crystals are plates about one millimeter in diameter.

To prepare a ceramic, the crystals are finely ground and mixed with 2 to 6% of a binder such as ''Halowax'' or polymethyl methacrylate in organic solution. The dried mixture is pressed into the desired shape at a pressure of several tons per square inch and fired one to two hours at some temperature between 1300 and 1500° C.

A somewhat lower firing temperature can be used if up to 5% of a mineralizer such as borax, $MgCl_2$ or $CaCl_2$ is incorporated before pressing. For use in electrical devices, silver electrodes are fired or evaporated onto the appropriate sample surfaces.

The uses of ferroelectric ceramics stem directly from their characteristic properties and are presented below in outline form. Most of the applications listed have until now employed barium titanate as the ferroelectric. Presumably, however, any of the newer materials would be applicable, with advantages or disadvantages depending upon the particular case.

Applications of Ferroelectric Ceramics

Listed below are applications of ferroelectric ceramics based on their useful properties. In each case the property is listed first followed by the application related to that property.

High Dielectric Constant—Capacitors. Already discussed in the series on titanate ceramics by Larry J. Ruffner (Chapters II, III, IV). Most of the barium titanate produced goes into this type of use.

Curie Temperature—1. Control devices utilizing the abrupt change in dielectric constant at the Curie temperature. Solid solutions of ferroelectrics

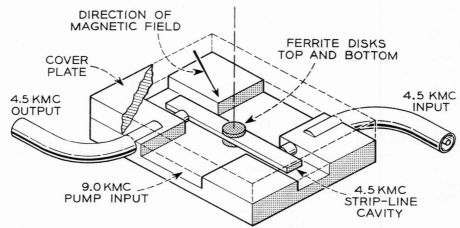

Diagram of an experimental ferrite microwave amplifier which was built at Bell Telephone Laboratories.

make it possible to have such peaks at virtually any temperature between absolute zero and 750° C. 2. Catalysis. Some work has been done which demonstrates the catalytic effect of certain ferroelectrics at their Curie Temperatures on gaseous oxidation reactions.

Nonlinearity—1. Dielectric amplifiers. Single crystals have an advantage over ceramics. 2. Information storage elements for electronic computers. Single crystals are preferable although some work has been done with ceramics having large, partially oriented crystals. 3. Miscellaneous electronic circuit applications such as frequency modulation, frequency stabilization, voltage stabilization.

Piezoelectricity—1. Ultrasonic generators for sonar, emulsification, precipitation, cleaning, drilling. 2. Loudspeakers, relays, thickness gauges, viscosimeters. 3. Vibration and acceleration measurement, force and roughness gauges, microphones, phonograph pickups.

Wide-ranging as they are, these practical applications of ferroelectric materials cannot help but be greatly multiplied in time. This follows merely from the fact that so few of the known ferroelectrics have as yet been exploited, and presumably individual material peculiarities will lead to additional uses. Compounding this with the fact that new ferroelectrics will continue to be discovered leads to the conclusion that this area of electrical materials is destined to become a very important one.

REFERENCES FOR CHAPTER XII

A. GENERAL

Anderson, P. W., ''Theory of Ferroelectric Behavior of Barium Titanate,'' Ceramic Age, 57 (1951) 29.

Devonshire, A. F., ''Theory of Ferroelectrics'', Advances in Physics, 3 (1954) 86.

von Hippel, A., ''Dielectrics and Waves,'' J. Wiley, N. Y., 1954.

B. MATERIALS

1. Shirane, G. and Hoshino, S., J. Phys. Soc. Japan, 6 (1951) 265.
2. Smolenskii, G. A., Proc. Acad. Sci. U.S.S.R., 70 (1950) 405.
3. Schweinler, H. C., Phys. Rev., 87 (1952) 5.
4. Youngblood, J., Bull, Am. Phys. Soc., 39 (1955) 62.
5. Devonshire, A. F., Brit. Elec. All. Ind. Res. Assoc., Tech. Report L/T298, 1953.
6. Shirane, G., Sawaguchi, E., and Takagi, Y., J. Phys. Soc. Japan, 6 (1951) 333.
7. Smolenskii, G. A. and Agranovskaya, A. I., Proc. Acad. Sci. U.S.S.R., 97 (1954) 237.
8. Sawada, S. and Nomura, S., J. Phys. Soc. Japan, 6 (1951) 192.
9. Mathias, B. and Remeika, J., Phys. Rev., 76 (1949) 1886.
10. Jona, F., Shirane, G., and Pepinsky, R., Phys. Rev., 97 (1955) 1584.
11. Shirane, G., Newnham, R., and Pepinsky, R., Phys. Rev., 96 (1954) 581.
12. Goodman, G., J. Am. Cer. Soc., 36 (1953) 368.
13. Jona, F., Shirane, G., and Pepinsky, R., Phys. Rev., 98 (1955) 903.
14. Mathias, B. T., Phys. Rev., 75 (1949) 1771.
15. Hulm, J. K., Mathias, B. T. and Long, E. A., Phys. Rev., 79 (1950) 885.
16. Smolenskii, G. A. and Kozhevnikova, N. V., Proc. Acad. Sci. U.S.S.R., 76 (1951) 519.
17. Sawada, S., Phys. Rev., 91 (1953) 1010.
18. Tranbe, K., Baldwin, W. J., and Best, C. A., Ceramic Age, 65 (1955) 9.
19. Mathias, B. T., U. S. Patent 2,598,707.

CHAPTER XIII

APPARENT MICROSCOPIC STRUCTURE OF HIGH ALUMINA MATERIALS

R. P. DILLINGHAM

Consolidated Electrodynamics Corp.

Most of the electronic ceramic parts are metalized and built into vacuum tube assemblies and the tube manufacturers have been understandably very critical of alumina ceramics from the standpoint of vacuum tightness. It is, of course, a very unhappy experience to complete a complex and expensive tube which may be worth many thousands of dollars only to find that it is unsalable because of leakage at some point in its construction. The ceramic supplier is somewhat prone to feel that such leakage can most likely be traced to the metallizing and the ceramic-to-metal seals and brazes. In turn, the tube manufacturer is apt to feel that all is well here and that the leakage must undoubtedly be due to holes of some sort in the ceramic itself.

These feelings have led both the ceramics supplier and the tube development and fabricating people to look into the ceramic with hopes of finding some of the answers to their leakage problems. Many approaches have been used and are well known in the industry. Actual testing of parts for leakage is, of course, a good approach but unfortunately the techniques are difficult and the time required is unduly long for production purposes. Some investigators have sought a more direct approach by examining the ceramic with dyes, different kinds of X-rays and by looking at polished samples under various magnifications.

Possible Leakage Sources

When an alumina ceramic surface, whether it be ground or "as-fired," is magnified, the observer at once notices that it has voids in it. In looking for possible causes of leakage, it is understandable that the tube manufacturer would be very interested in these holes in the ceramic and might immediately wonder if it is possible that they might extend from one of the ceramic surfaces to the other or through a complex system of inner connections produce a minute leakage path which would be sufficient to cause tubes to go bad. Because ceramic envelopes and the like are usually cylindrical, many of the investigators sawed pieces of the ceramic out of the part and ground them flat in order to get a better optical field for their microscopic studies. A number of investigators have reported that there was considerable variation in the microscopic structure of alumina ceramic and that some samples seemed to be full of holes while others seemed to be relatively free from holes or pores. As a result of this, a thorough study of the entire matter was made at the research laboratory of Coors Porcelain Co. in order first to determine what the situation actually was and second, to develop a measure by which ceramic might be evaluated for electronic use.

As the investigation progressed, it was learned that there was no established method for polishing and that different investigators used different methods and frequently the some investigator did not rigidly adhere to a definite sample preparation technique. Certain investigators felt that they were able to evaluate the quality of an alumina body section with no finishing other than a sawed surface. Others felt that finish must be good but that a high degree of polish was unimportant. Still others felt that the evaluation was more a matter of experience gained from looking at a large number of samples and some mental correlation of this visual impression with impressions of tube quality.

Investigate Preparation of Sample

Accordingly, among many phases which were investigated was the preparation of the sample itself. It was soon learned that the apparent structure was greatly affected by the method of sample preparation and that two samples could not be properly compared unless the preparation techniques were identical. It was also noted that a sample could be made to look very good—that is relatively free from large or connecting holes— or very poor by different polishing procedures. Without going into the many details of this part of the study, it was soon apparent that much of the structural appearance was due to polishing and that most of the bad samples were actually quite good, when they were properly prepared. It was found that poor appearance was usually due to poor preparation and that small pores in the ceramic could be made to appear to be large craters with connection from one crater to another due to tearing out of the edges of the pores during the various lapping operations.

A satisfactory technique for sample preparation resulted from this study and through the use of this method of preparing samples, much closer control of the ceramic manufacturing processes was achieved and the users in turn were able to evaluate shipments of our ceramics both more quickly and more accurately. In addition, the development of this method of evaluation provides a valuable measuring tool by which research samples can undergo comparison.

Outline of Polishing Procedure

The polishing procedure which is briefly outlined below will give reproducible samples of adequate finish:

1. Cut a sample $\frac{1}{4}$x$\frac{1}{4}$x$\frac{1}{2}''$ long from the ceramic sample or part.
2. Mount in Bakelite using a Buehler mounting press or equivalent. This facilitates handling of sample during polishing.
3. Using a 220 grit water cooled diamond cup wheel, faceoff sample to obtain flatness.

4. Using a 500 grit water cooled diamond cup wheel, smooth sample face preparatory to first lapping operation.

5. The first lapping operation is done on a straight grained hard maple lap mounted on the Buehler polisher. Each lapping or polishing operation is done in two steps:
   (1) Slow speed at 400 R.P.M. for 1 minute.
   (2) High speed at 1200 R.P.M. for 1 minute.
   Fourteen micron diamond paste is used in first operation as the polishing agent. If any rough spots are noted, the above time-speed sequences are repeated. The sample is moved about on the lap to prevent burning of the lap surface and deep scratches in the sample. Clean sample thoroughly with acetone to remove all diamond paste thus preventing contamination of the next lap.

6. The second lapping operation is done on a silk covered bronze lap, using 6 micron diamond paste as the polishing agent, and following the same time-speed sequences as above. Again the sample is cleaned thoroughly to prevent contamination of the next lap.

7. The 3rd lapping operation is done as before using 3 micron diamond paste as the polishing agent and the same time-speed sequence.

8. The fourth and final polishing operation is conducted as before, with the emphasis on lighter pressure and more movement to completely eliminate scratches, tears, etc. One micron diamond paste is used as the polishing agent and produces the final mirror finish that is desired.

A Word of Caution

A word of caution—do not overcharge laps with diamond compound as the edges of the crystals and voids will be rounded by an excessive amount of compound thus giving a false impression.

In conclusion, to obtain properly polished samples which can be evaluated to provide research or control information, the samples must be processed as nearly the same way as possible. The polishing method as outlined is simple enough so that this may be accomplished with comparative ease. The use of the 14, 6, 3, and 1-micron diamond compounds provides the cutting action necessary for high alumina materials, at a speed which is satisfactory for production control. The samples, after polishing, may be compared directly, and thus give valuable research and production control information.

CHAPTER XIV

ALUMINUM OXIDE CERAMICS

DANIEL W. LUKS

Frenchtown Porcelain Co.

How shall we classify aluminum oxide ceramics? Most, although not all ceramics, contain alumina to some extent; hence, where do we draw the line between them and the everyday, run-of-the-mill ceramics that have been produced throughout the world for the past few thousand years? As far as the trade is concerned, there seems to be no distinct line of demarcation between alumina and other types of ceramics, so we are free to promote our own interpretation.

Classic Phase Diagram

Possibly the best way to describe alumina ceramics is to call upon the classic alumina-silica phase diagram by Bowen & Greig, shown in Fig. 1. On this diagram we see a division between phases free of corundum and of those containing various amounts of it, at the mullite ($3Al_2O_3$-$2SiO_2$) line. From this we prefer to call those formulations containing more alumina than the amount required by the mullite formula, alumina ceramics. This is a matter of choice and it does not follow that alumina in smaller amounts will be of no benefit when incorporated in a ceramic formula.

A good illustration of this is the well known fact that superior (at that time) vitrified spark plug insulators containing crystalline alumina as corundum, were in wide usage prior to World War I. The free alumina here augmented mechanical impact resistance and counteracted destruction due to thermal shock.

As the percentage of alumina in the ceramic approaches 100% there seems to be a preference toward calling these compositions ''high alumina'' ceramics. The high aluminas, by their very nature, necessarily contain relatively small amounts of other ingredients, and if properly compounded and matured, display the physical and electrical properties of pure alumina itself.

In some cases the addition of the proper minor components decidedly improves certain properties, mostly electrical, beyond values inherent in alumina alone. Most of the alumina ceramics on the market today, in order to take full advantage of the beneficial properties of the parent mineral, are formulated to contain about 80% to 95% aluminum oxide by chemical analysis. The majority of the alumina is combined in crystal form, or to lesser degree has become part of the glass film necessary to statisfactory intercrystalline growth and vitrification.

It may be seen above that from a technical point of view, an alumina ceramic while comprising mainly one crystalline phase, is nevertheless a complicated structure, each integral part of which plays an important role.

High Mechanical Strength

The outstanding features of aluminum oxide ceramics are high mechanical strength, high thermal conductivity and excellent electrical properties, particularly dielectric loss factor. In addition to these, extreme hardness, resistance to chemical attack and high relative density make it an ideal material for industrial operations.

Mechanical strength is the biggest seller, and seems to be the most popular property in all fields. Electrical insulators of every sort, be they spacers, terminals, capacitors, envelopes, windows, or standoff types, require exceptional resistance to mechanical shock from vibration and impact. There is a tendency too, in the modern manufacturing world, to speed up assembly operations to the utmost to increase production and to reduce costs, with the result that the ceramic parts must be sufficiently strong to resist breakage under these added strains applied to them.

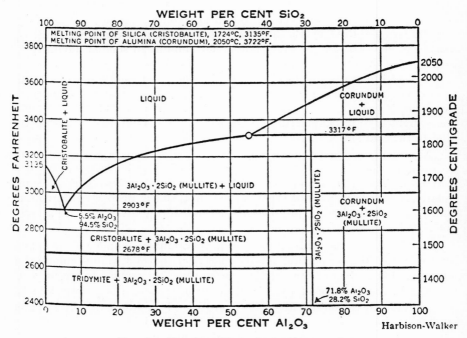

Fig. 1. Alumina-silica phase diagram by Bowen and Grieg with corrections by Schairer.

First Used for Spark Plugs

The first field to employ fully aluminum oxide ceramic insulation was, without a doubt, spark plugs. As previously mentioned, aluminum oxide as corundum has been a part of spark plug insulation formulations for more than 35 years; however, it was not until the early 1930's when it was recognized that a new and superior type of high voltage insulation could be manufactured with the aid of relatively high percentages of aluminum oxide, and which, when so produced, was readily suited to the then new trend in automotive engine design.

Tetraethyl lead in modern gasolines, introduced to reduce or eliminate the knock indigenous to high compression ratios, higher combustion temperatures and increased corrosion all furnished the need for spark plug insulations having superior qualities.

Alumina's comparatively high thermal conductivity rate permitted the design of longer spark plug insulator firing tips, which in turn reduced carbon and other deposits normally accrued through gasoline combustion. High mechanical strength sponsored rugged assembly methods with tighter and more reliable units the result.

Also alumina's excellent abrasion resistance is nicely adapted to sand blast cleaning of firing tips, and its high "hot electrical resistance" insures

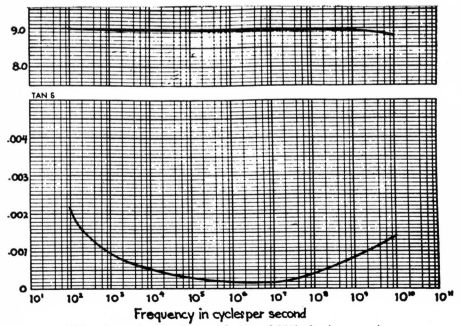

Dielectric constants and power factors of 94% alumina ceramics.

a fat spark at the electrodes during operation. As might be expected, thermal shock resistance, aided by superior thermal conductivity, is another important property offered the spark plug industry by alumina.

Envelopes for Power Tubes

A most recent case where aluminum oxide ceramics illustrated their worth is in their use for envelopes to house and protect high frequency power tubes. Due to outstanding dielectric properties, these envelopes are popular for use from radio frequency to ultra high frequency ranges.

Mechanical strength is also very important here in that the envelopes are commonly metalized and brazed to complemental metal parts or are fastened to them by means of pressure seals. In the former case the ceramic must withstand any strains imposed upon it by unequal contraction of the component parts during cooling after brazing. In the latter, the ceramic envelope is subjected to either a shrink fit or several tons pressure during the squeezing of the metal components into place around the ceramic.

Alumina ceramics, being highly inert to chemical reaction at elevated temperatures, lend themselves neatly to the ever increasing bake-out temperatures required in all electronic devices to remove traces of harmful elements which might, later on, destroy operating efficiency. These bake-out temperatures today commonly reach 600° C. and experimentally as high as 900°, where requirements become more exacting.

Alumina windows are also becoming popular for magnetrons developing power sufficient to destroy mica or glass. The requirements here are similar to those of the envelopes except that in this case the electron beams directly penetrate the windows, which must be very uniform dimensionally and constitutionally to avoid wave interruption and subsequent breakdown.

Radio frequency tube spacers have for some time been made of alumina ceramics. However, these are almost always sufficiently porous to allow thorough evacuation of any trapped gases after assembly. While parts made in this manner must have excellent dielectric properties at elevated temperatures, particularly in filament supports, they do not compare directly with the vitreous types used for envelopes in other high voltage purposes.

Additional Uses of Materials

Additional uses of vitreous alumina ceramics, dependent upon good dielectric properties and mechanical strength, are for high voltage standoff insulators, support rings, multiple unit capacitors, bushings, condenser shafts and printed circuit bases. In special applications the above types are metalized and hermetically sealed into their respective assemblies.

The recrystallized corundum developed during the firing of alumina ceramics lends to the resultant body its extreme hardness. In fact bodies containing very high percentages of alumina become as hard as corundum itself. This feature makes them desirable for other than electrical uses, and they have been found most satisfactory when made into equipment

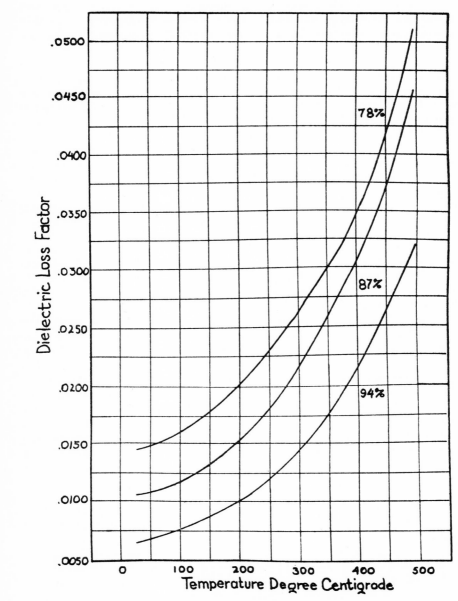

Temperature vs. dielectric loss factor
of Al₂O₃ ceramics, 1000-meg. frequency.

subject to severe abrasion. Examples are sand blast nozzles, spraying nozzles and spray-drying whirl chambers. It has been found by actual comparison under like conditions that high alumina sandblast nozzles will outlast the conventional "white iron" ones by as much as a 10 to 1 ratio.

Wear resistant inserts for extrusion dies and thread and wire guides are made of this hard material with excellent results. Pump parts such as plunger casings, shaft sleeves, pressure seats, ball checks for valves and ejectors, take advantage of alumina's unexcelled abrasion and chemical resistance.

TABLE I
Properties of high-alumina ceramics

Property	78% Alumina	87% Alumina	94% Alumina
Type of body	Alumina-mullite	Alumina	Alumina
True specific gravity	3.33	3.61	3.88
Bulk specific gravity	2.97	3.44	3.76
Weight, lb./in.^{3}	0.107	0.124	0.127
Water absorption, %	0	0	0
Pore volume, %	10.9	4.7	3.2
Linear coefficient of thermal expansion— per deg. C.,			
25–100° C.	4.40×10^{-6}	5.33×10^{-6}	3.60×10^{-6}
25–400° C.	5.72×10^{-6}	6.85×10^{-6}	6.11×10^{-6}
25–700° C.	6.42×10^{-6}	7.42×10^{-6}	7.29×10^{-6}
Coefficient of thermal conductivity, cal/sec/cm^2/cm/deg. C.	0.0095	.0145	0.0180
Softening temperature, F.	3000°	3580°	3500°
,, ,, C.	1649°	1971°	1927°
Tensile strength, psi	11,000	13,000	16,000
Compressive strength, psi	120,000	145,000	190,000
Flexural strength, psi	25,000	29,000	36,000
Impact resistance, Charpy,* in.-lb.	5.1	5.8	6.2
Static modulus of elasticity, psi	20.9×10^{-6}	30.0×10^{-6}	34.1×10^{-6}
TE value,† F.	1310°	1380°	1470°
,, ,, C.	710°	749°	799°
Volume resistivity megohm/cm^3			
400° C.	133	220	195
500° C.	25	34	53
600° C.	4.7	7.0	14.4
700° C.	1.3	1.8	3.8
800° C.	0.4	0.6	1.0
Dielectric strength, v/mil	200	200	200
Dielectric constant, 10^6 cycles	7.0	8.4	9.2
Power factor, 10^6 cycles	0.0014	0.00086	0.00035
Loss factor, 10^6 cycles	0.010	0.007	0.003

* ½ in. diam. rods between 4 in. centers. † Temperature at which 1 cu. cm. of material has resistance of 1 megohm.

TABLE II
Chemical analyses of commercial Al₂O₃ ceramics

	1	2	3	4	5	6
	(%)	(%)	(%)	(%)	(%)	(%)
Al₂O₃	92.08	85.64	89.62	92.56	92.95	82.82
SiO₂	2.97	10.36	6.48	4.43	3.60	8.30
CaO	1.20	1.30	1.17	1.90	2.60	1.05
MgO	1.55	2.45	2.60	.85	....	4.40
ZrO₂	2.02	....	....	....	....	2.18
Fe₂O₃	.03	.02	.04	.04	.38	....
Na₂O	....	....	....	....	.34	.28
K₂O	....	....	....	....	.04	.30
TiO₂	.12	.23	.12	.12	.06	.18
MnO	...	.04	.02	.02	....	....
BeO	....	....	....	....	....	.24
	99.97	100.04	100.05	99.92	99.97	99.75

Thread and plug gages made from alumina have long life and hold their contours uniformly throughout. Metal lathe and milling machine cutting tools have been made from alumina ceramics in Europe for the past 20 years, and they are now gaining favor in this country.

Alumina Grinding Media Superior

It has been shown that alumina pebble mill grinding media are superior to the conventional types in both rate of comminution and wear resistance. Alumina media, being of greater unit weight, will handle high density products much better than the comparatively low weight silica media. They can today be obtained in several shapes including spheroids, ellipsoids and cylinders. For best results the mill linings should be of the same composition as the media.

It should be remembered that the compositions of various alumina ceramics differ somewhat according to their "end uses." The higher the alumina content the greater the wear resistance, and to augment this, in some cases, special oxides such as cobalt, nickel and chrome are considered aids to superior characteristics.

Pure aluminum oxide melts at 3722° F. according to the literature. Aluminum oxide ceramic compositions soften and deform between 3000° and 3600° F.; the higher the alumina content the higher the softening temperature. It may be seen from this that bodies of this type are all able to withstand extreme temperatures without serious effect upon them, provided the heat is not applied or withdrawn too rapidly. Like all high strength ceramics, the mechanical strength of the aluminum oxide type is impaired by thermal shock conditions. The strength loss is cumulative, increasing with each cycle until failure occurs.

CHAPTER XV

HOW ALUMINUM OXIDE CERAMICS ARE MADE

Daniel W. Luks

Frenchtown Porcelain Co.

The basic raw material for alumina ceramics is aluminum oxide in some form, and it is a matter of personal preference which type is employed in any one composition. Four general types predominate. They are hydrated aluminum oxide, fine grained calcined alumina, sintered or tabular alumina and electrically fused alumina. There are several grades of each on the market and they vary in crystal or particle size and in their chemical composition.

The main impurity in manufactured aluminum oxide is sodium oxide, the content of which ranges between .02% and .50%. Aluminas containing high alkali content are perfectly satisfactory for use in compositions designed for mechanical purposes; however, it is quite necessary that the material with the lowest percentage of alkali be incorporated in formulas from which electronic type ceramics are manufactured. This is particularly true in the case of spark plug insulations which demand high, hot electrical resistance and again in certain parts used for ultra high frequency electrical applications.

Raw Material Particle Size Important

Since it is necessary to reduce the alumina particles to extremely small size for proper density, the original particle size of the raw material is an important feature. The basic particle size of the hydrate is extremely small and may be less than 1 micron in diameter, while the calcined alumina particle diameter may be as low as 2 microns or as great as 40 microns depending upon the effect of impurities and the heat treatment to which it has been subjected during manufacture. The sintered aluminas are produced as agglomerated spheroids or cylinders about 3/4" diameter. Fused alumina occurs as a molten magma which has no definite size or shape before milling operations.

The second most important part of aluminum oxide ceramic compositions is silica and the most popular method of introducing it is by the addition of clay or double silicates such as talc. It is rarely added as silicon dioxide and then only in very finely divided form.

Since a certain, but small amount of glass is very necessary for proper vitrification of alumina ware, a third component must be introduced, either as a distinct portion of the batch, or as an impurity. Examples are mineralizers such as iron and titanium oxides, the alkalies, or alkaline earths.

The method chosen for mixing and blending aluminum oxide compositions depends first upon the type of oxide selected, and second, upon the end use for which the ceramic is produced. Conventional methods common to the ceramic industry are universally employed. These comprise dry or wet pebble milling the aluminum oxide either before or after it has been incorporated in the formula.

Milling with Steel Balls

An early procedure operating in Germany was to wet mill the aluminum oxide with steel balls in steel lined mills, with final washing of the material with hydrochloric acid to remove iron contamination incurred during the processing. On the face of it, this appears to be an expensive operation; however, by this method the most densely sintered alumina is rapidly ground to fine particle size by the relatively heavy steel balls, and the acid wash not only removes the iron, but in addition materially reduces the alkalies and other impurities.

The other ingredients in an aluminum oxide ceramic formula may be added during the primary milling of the alumina or may be wet or dry pebble milled after the primary operation. Other methods of mixing are blunging and dry mixing. After wet milling or blunging it is common practice to remove the water through use of spray drying.

Typical ultra-thin AlSiMag alumina ceramics for electron tubes and other exacting applications, made by American Lava Corp., Chattanooga, Tenn. Many important advantages are claimed in use of these components.

In line with general ceramic practice, the wet pebble milled and blunged compositions are the most intimately mixed, whereas those blended in the popular muller-type "dry mixer," are least. On the other hand the dry mixers are preferred for blending moisture and binders with the previously formulated and processed material compositions.

Three Types of Binders Used

Three general types of binders are used with aluminum oxide compositions to aid in "green" or unfired strength and to facilitate machining operations. They are the water soluble types such as dextrin, gum arabic, polyvinyl alcohol; the water swelling, gelatinous types, which are sometimes partly soluble and which are represented by gum tragacanth, carboxy methyl-cellulose and starches; and finally the suspension and emulsion types which include the very popular wax emulsions and the less known resin emulsions.

As a class, the water soluble binders afford the greatest increase in green mechanical strength; however, they tend to migrate, making prefired machining difficult and costly, and in addition at times causing a disintegration or shelling of the areas containing the accumulated concentrations of binder.

On the other hand, the second group, the water swelling types, create plasticity, bond strength and general uniform distribution throughout the unfired mass. Occasionally high shrinkage results, and at times trouble is encountered due to slow moisture travel through the gelatinous bond, with fractured ware the result.

Emulsion Type Binder

The third and last class of binder, the emulsion type, has received much acclaim due to appreciable gain in internal lubrication, a factor most im-

Typical all-ceramic envelope tube.

portant to low clay, high internal friction alumina mixtures. They present comparatively slight bond strength unless present in large proportions; nevertheless, migration is nil and structure very uniform throughout. Occasional difficulties are emulsion breakdown due to aging or excess temperature, coagulation due to chemical incompatibility and incomplete distribution throughout the ceramic mixture.

Aluminum oxide ceramics are molded, shaped and machined by methods ordinarily called upon by the ceramic trades. They include dry pressing, wet pressing, isostatic pressing, extrusion and machining, casting and injection molding.

Most Economical Production Methods

Dry pressing and wet pressing are perhaps the most economical methods for producing large quantities of complicated shapes. The two processes differ mainly in moisture content present in clay "dust," it being 16%–20% moisture on a dry basis in wet pressed clay, and 1%–3% in the method using dry pressed clay.

The shapes made by either of these processes are finished and ready to fire as they come from the die, with the possible exception of fin removal, and in this respect simulate operations well known to the steatite and electrical porcelain trades.

TABLE IV
Patented aluminum oxide ceramic formulas

	1	2	3	4	5
Alumina	90	96.5	91.68	....	95
Tabular corundum	....	....	......	75	....
Magnesia	4	....	......	....	....
Whiting	2	1.5	2.57	....	....
Zircon	2	....	......	....	3.5
Beryl	1	....	......	....	....
Boric acid	1	....	......	....	....
Talc	....	2.0	1.25	....	1.5
Clay	....	....	3.50	....	....
Chromium oxide	....	....	1.00	....	....
English ball clay	....	....	......	15	....
Calcium phosphate	....	....	......	5	....
Florida kaolin	....	....	......	5	....

The dies for pressing aluminum oxide "dust" are almost always made of sintered tungsten carbide, since ordinary hard steel dies wear far beyond commerical tolerance in very short order. Die cost is consequently two to three times greater than usual.

Isostatic Pressing Is Adaptable

Isostatic pressing is a much younger addition to the ceramic trade processes and is nicely adaptable to the production of alumina ceramics since hydraulic presure is applied equally on all sides to the pulverized body by means of a flexible casing. This eliminates die friction and creates a body of uniform density throughout.

The external portion of the pressed blank must be shaped by machinery or dry grinding, which is an added cost above ordinary dry pressing operations; however, this is compensated for to some extent by the ability to press the clay neatly around threaded or otherwise complicated fixtures, which is either impossible or costly to carry out by other means. The moisture content of "dust" for isostatic pressing is low and similar to that for dry pressing. Sometimes binders are added; particularly in the case of very high aluminum oxide contents.

A much older method of production is also applicable to the handling of aluminum oxide ceramics. This is extrusion and subsequent machining to shape. In the simplest cases, such as rods and uniform diameter tubes, the alumina mixes are plasticized with water, which content varies between 16%–20%, and are extruded, dried on supports and finally cut into shape with the aid of abrasive saws.

To effect more complicated structures, blanks are extruded, dried, occasionally calcined to red heat for added strength and either shaped with

Continuous firing of alumina ceramics at temperatures up to 3200° F. is accomplished with this equipment.

profile abrasion wheel or machined by lathe methods. Evacuation of the clay mass has today, almost without exception, become a part of the extrusion process. Highest densities and uniform internal structure are the result of this procedure.

To one acquainted with the standard ceramic procedures little need be said concerning casting aluminum oxide ware. The methods are the same as these employed for casting refractories or ordinary high-clay slips, the only difference being the relatively large proportion of inert, nonplastic material in the aluminum oxide ceramic slip.

Usual Deflocculants Employed

The usual deflocculants are employed—sodium silicate, sodium carbonate and sodium phosphates, all having the desire effects in reducing the water content to the minimum necessary for proper casting. Total concentrations of salt up to 1% of the dry weight of the ceramic mixture in the slip are acceptable, but it should be borne in mind that excess alkali is harmful to dielectric properties of the fired ceramic.

Casting has the disadvantage in refusing to conform to the close tolerances today demanded by the electronic and electrical ceramics trade, hence is limited in its application. Its main use is in the production of shapes too large to be made by other means or which must necessarily assume the shape of a thin shell conforming to complicated contours.

Injection Molding Sometimes Used

An unusual, additional method of forming ceramics and one which is occasionally chosen for the high alumina types due to their "shortness," is injection or a transfer molding. Here 10% to 20% of a thermoplastic or thermosetting resin, such as polystyrene or phenol formaldehyde compositions, is mixed with pulverized ceramic body by means of cold milling, hot milling or solution distribution.

The resulting mixtures are heated to plasticize, then, in the case of the thermoplastic binder, injection molded into a cold die of desired shape. If transfer molded, they are injected into a hot die and held until polymerization of the resin is complete, usually a matter of 1 to 3 minutes at approximately 350° F. Occasionally, simple trimming or machining is resorted to before firing.

The drying of aluminum oxide ceramic ware is comparatively simple and rapid due to low plastic material content and resultant minor drying shrinkage; nevertheless, it is important that the ware be completely dried at a temperature high enough to boil away any uncombined moisture, to lessen chances of destruction during the first part of the firing cycle. If wax and similar binders have been employed in large quantity, it is sometimes beneficial to raise drying temperatures to 300–400° F. Methods of this sort are of particular interest where machining after drying is resorted to.

TABLE III

Chemical analyses of representative aluminum oxide materials

	Alumina hydrate #C-730	Calcined alumina #A-10	Sintered alumina #T-61	Electrically fused alumina #38500 & #38900
Al_2O_3	64.40	99.50	99.50+	Balance
Combined H_2O	34.90	....	....	....
Free H_2O	.21	.10	....	....
Na_2O	.45	.10	.02	<.02
SiO_2	.05	.05	.02	<.02
CaO	....	....	....	<.05
MgO	....	....	....	<.05
Fe_2O_3	.02	.04	.03	.06
ZrO_2	....	....	....	Trace
C	....	....	....	<.01
Ignition loss	....	.15	....	....
Information source	(a)	(a)	(a)	(b)
	100.03	99.94	99.57+	(100.00)

(a) Aluminum Co. of America   (b) Norton Co.

Firing Is Troublesome

The firing of alumina ceramics is perhaps the most troublesome operation encountered throughout their manufacture. Tunnel kilns are preferred since they hold a more uniform temperature pattern throughout the firing cycle and are more economical for large production purposes. However, periodic kilns can be employed satisfactorily and are chosen when relatively small quantities of ware are to be fired at any one temperature or when numerous different compositions requiring individual firing treatment are to be processed.

During the early days of aluminum oxide ware production there was a tendency to manufacture compositions requiring very high maturing temperatures. It was rapidly seen that excellent high alumina compositions containing small, but sufficient, quantities of auxiliary fluxes could be produced at much lower firing temperatures with equivalent results. Maturing temperatures today rarely exceed 3000° F., whereas they originally approached the fusion point of aluminum oxide itself.

Encounter Refractory Problems

Most of the common ceramic refractories such as mullite and zircon tend to attack alumina ceramics during firing so it is necessary to use furniture made of high alumina compositions, or to protect the ware from setter contact by means of hard-burned or fused alumina sand.

Large alumina shapes must be supported on true surfaces, as high alumina bodies tend to soften near maturity and assume the contour of the refactory support. This is particularly important where close tolerances are to be met.

Small shapes can be fired comparatively rapidly. The preheating portion of the firing cycle can be a straight line progression and quite rapid due to lack of plastic or water-bearing materials. Due to alumina's relatively good thermal shock resistance, the cooling portion of the firing cycle can also be of rapid and uniform slope. A controlling factor here is kiln furniture life.

Hot Zone Most Important

The hot zone where vitrification takes place is the most important one for many reasons. In contrast to ordinary ceramic bodies, aluminum oxide ceramics are mainly crystalline alumina with relatively small amounts of other crystals, and a very minor quantity of glass. The glass acts as a medium for inter-crystalline growth throughout the body, so it is important that the correct amount of glass be present, and that the maturing temperature chosen be sufficient to make the glass active, and at the same time low enough to prevent overfiring or squatting.

The proper way to bring about correct maturity is therefore to attain a minimum temperature and then hold it long enough to complete the body reaction.

CHAPTER XVI

FINISHING AND TESTING ALUMINUM OXIDE CERAMICS

Daniel W. Luks
Frenchtown Porcelain Co.

On the average, dimensional tolerances range near $\pm 1\%$ with a minimum of $\pm.005''$. In some cases, particularly on very small parts, any one dimension may be held closer without special postfiring processing. The tendency has been in recent years, particularly for parts designed for electronic assemblies, to demand much closer tolerances in the range $\pm .001''$ or in some specialized cases, a span of $.001''$. These requirements are being met with the aid of diamond filled grinding wheels and in extreme cases, by using diamond abrasive hones.

Standard metal grinding lathes, single disc, double disc and centerless grinders fitted with diamond wheels have been adopted for finish grinding aluminum oxide ceramics. The fineness of the cut and the smoothness of the resulting surfaces are dependent upon the particle size of the diamonds employed. For initial cuts, 60 to 100 mesh particles are preferred, while 400 mesh grains are used for finishing.

Need 3000-Mesh Particles

Honing to extremely close tolerances and to highly uniform reflectance surfaces calls for diamond particles up to 3000 mesh (4 to 8 microns). These last are generally applied in the form of a water slurry to a soft iron plate, which revolves in contact with the ceramic undergoing the grinding.

Some grinding can be accomplished by silicon carbide abrasive wheels; however, these wheels tend to wear away and lose their grains so rapidly that it is difficult to keep track of dimension by means of the calibrated vernier feed mechanism of the grinding machine.

Silicon carbide abrasives also cut more slowly and require much more pressure against the object being cut.

Diamond wheels cut very rapidly and at first glance it would seem that grinding cost would be low. This is not true, however, since firing warpage and normal shrinkage tolerances make it necessary to incorporate within the dimension of the fired piece considerable overage, to insure a completely true ground surface.

Why Alumina Is Glazed

Some alumina ware is glazed to afford a smooth surface on the finished part without the aid of finish grinding or polishing. Glazes present the same properties here that they do on other types of ceramic ware, and these include facilitation of dirt removal, but in the case of electrical or electronic products they must also present a refractory surface which will withstand for long periods of time high ambient temperatures, and in addition must resist reduction and must present excellent electrical surface resistance under either humid or dry conditions.

Both single fire and double or glost fire glazes are used on alumina ware. The former must necessarily be very refractory and in some cases

Checking dimensions and contours of aluminum oxide ceramics using the projection method.

will create harmful proximity effects within the ware itself. Compositions are generally the same as those used on high quality electrical porcelain, but in addition other processes such as "vapor" types, soluble salts and even chemically leached glazes have been proposed in the literature.

Metallizing Readily Done

Aluminum oxide ceramics, mainly due to their high strength and fairly high thermal expansion coefficient, lend themselves nicely to metallizing.

Two-stage metallizing is typified by the Telefunken molybdenum-iron process wherein a mixture containing these two metals in powder form is painted upon the matured ceramic and fired to a point just below the maturity temperature of the ceramic, in the presence of a protective atmosphere such as hydrogen. The metals combine with the surface of the ceramic and form a strong bond upon the surface.

Either copper or nickel plating is applied and sintered, after which metal fittings may be soldered, again in a protective atmosphere, to metallized portions by means of hard solders such as copper-silver eutectic, fine silver or oxygen free copper.

Single stage metallizing is carried out with the aid of titanium hydride or zirconium hydride combined with cooper-silver or other hard solders, applied to the junction between the ceramic and its component metal parts. Vacuum is preferred for this operation; however, extremely pure and moisture free protective gases are also applicable.

Use Care in Choosing Metal Alloys

Since the expansion coefficients of metal alloys vary widely according to their compositions, care should be taken to choose the right one from which to manufacture the metal parts to be fastened to the ceramic. There are some exceptions to expansion match; for instance, copper is widely used for fittings despite its relatively high expansion, since it is very flexible and readily distorts to fit the ceramic during the temperature change which takes place.

Physically, aluminum oxide ceramics, after firing and finish-grinding operations, are examined first visually, then under a wide field magnifying glass to discover discernible flaws or extraordinary appearance. In this test certain aids such as sodium vapor illumination or penetrating fluorescent solutions detectable under ultra-violet light are utilized to accentuate defects.

In rare cases standard specimens fired adjacent to the part in question are later thin-sectioned and examined under a high powered mineralogical microscope to determine degree of maturity.

Meeting Strength Requirement

Parts for heavy duty mechanical uses are often actually mounted in testing machines exerting either torsional, compressive or tensional strain upon the part to insure meeting a set minimum strength requirement. This sort of test is carried out either on each piece in the entire lot, or on so many pieces per hundred, chosen at random.

Electrical testing is generally a flash-over spark test employing a high frequency power source to insure internal flaw detection. In some cases close fitting electrodes are applied, and the voltage brought to a certain specified minimum on each piece in the lot. Unfortunately, some shapes defy the use of an electrical breakdown test and in these cases visual or microscopic examination must be relied upon.

Some parts must not only be electrically sound but also vacuum tight. The degree of vacuum tightness governs the test, which may range from the ordinary air-leakage-under-pressure test to the very exact helium leak detector examination. Ordinarily, these last two devices are applied after partial or complete assembly.

Consider Design Factors

1. *Simplification*—Where cost is an important consideration, design of aluminum oxide ceramics should be as simple as possible. It is much easier to finish-grind a true cylinder or sleeve or simple disc than one with multiple bores or elliptical contours. It is generally more economical to produce two simple shapes to take the place of a complicated one. In designing assemblies start with a simplified ceramic nucleus about which may be placed the more easily fabricated metal parts.

2. *Tolerances*—Call for finished-ground surfaces only where absolutely necessary and then with only as close a tolerance as required. For instance plane parallel surfaces finished to a tolerance ± 1% are in a great many cases acceptable and are definitely much less costly than plane parallel surfaces ± .001″. The same logic may be applied to concentricity of inner and outer surfaces of the sleeves and tubes involved.

3. *Irregular Designs*—Warpage and cracking are the result of thin wall design and holes or counter bores placed too close together. Slender fin-like structures attached to heavy bases invite differential firing shrinkage and distortion. Holes placed at right angles to each other require special machining and hence are a luxury item.

On larger shapes sufficient body should be designed throughout to insure firing support. While it is possible to grind away external camber of a tube, it is practically impossible to grind the bore internally for any but the shortest distance.

4. *Contours*—The over-all strength of a ceramic design can be greatly increased by the use of fillets and radii in corners, and the resistance to chipping can be increased by the use of chamfers or radii at the edges. Sharp edges are prone to chip at the least impact and sharp corners have much less resistance and tensile strength than those protected by a radius.

CHAPTER XVII

SHAPING CERAMICS TO PRECISION TOLERANCES— PART 1

J. E. COMEFORO

Frenchtown Porcelain Co.

T. S. STANISLAW

Sylvania Electric Products, Inc.

Since antiquity the making of ceramics consisted of forming the desired shapes followed by a heating operation to impart the necessary mechanical strength and chemical resistance. The heating process results in reactions that also develop dense crystalline phases and usually a glass which assists in coalescing the particles and eliminating pores. Hence, the size of the fired ceramic is smaller than when formed. This firing shrinkage is the paramount obstacle in achieving close tolerances when working with conventionally fabricated ceramic shapes.

If ceramics could be readily machined after the firing operation the difficulty presented by shrinkage during the firing operation could largely be circumvented. They, then, could be worked and shaped to the same precision commonly expected with metals. The extreme brittleness and hardness of most ceramics has made this economically unfeasible except for very special applications.

The purpose of this chapter is to review the advances made during and since World War II in developing new ceramic compositions, improving existing techniques and controls and utilizing special grinding and shaping methods to make possible the maintenance of dimensional tolerances that had previously been considered impractical to attain.

These, then, are the *precision ceramics to be discussed.*

New Ceramic Types

Since the inception of the electrical industry, machined ceramics made from block talc have served as insulators. Block talc, commonly called lava by electrical engineers, was selected because it is readily machinable prior to firing, and, when fired, undergoes a length change of less than 2%, thereby minimizing the difficulty involved in achieving the desired dimensions.

As will be shown in this report, recent developments have greatly diminished the dependence of the electrical industry on block talc. Block talc possesses the advantageous characteristics of excellent machinability in the unfired state, low firing shrinkage, good electrical insulating qualities, and does not liberate or absorb gases when used in electronic tubes; it

88

TABLE I

Comparison of properties of block talc with phosphate-bonded talc, hot-pressed synthetic mica, and phosphate-bonded synthetic mica

Property	Natural Indian block	Phosphate-bonded talc dry pressed [a]	Hot pressed synthetic mica [c]	Synthetic mica phosphate bonded [d]
Specific gravity (gm/cc)				
Unfired	2.5	2.3–2.5	....	2.1–2.4
Fired	2.8	2.4–2.6	2.5–3.5	2.0–2.5
Water absorption (%)	2–3	3.5–9	0.05–10	3–10
Linear Firing shrinkage (%)	1.5–2.0	1.5–2.5	none	0.0–4
Flexural strength (psi)				
Unfired	....	200–400	10,000	200–500
Fired	9,000	4,500–7,000	....	5,000–9,000
Compressive strength (psi)				
Unfired	....	700–1,000	>35,000	n.d.
Fired	30,000	25,000–40,000	....	n.d.
Hardness (Mohs' scale)	1 [b]	1–2 [b]	2+ – 4+	2– – 3+
Dielectric constant (1 mc)				
room temperature	5.8	5.5	5.8	4–7
Power factor (1 mc)				
room temperature	0.03%	0.06%	0.03–0.3%	0.03–0.03%
200° C.	0.13	0.08	0.05–0.3	0.4 –0.6
350° C.	0.7	0.13	0.8 –1.0	1.1 –2.0

[a] All samples fired to 1,000° C. on 12-hour schedule, data from Comeforo, Breedlove, Thurnauer, etc., see reference number 1.
[b] Before firing.
[c] Commercially available from Brush Beryllium Co.
[d] Available from American Lava Corp

also finds considerable favor as a material for jigs and fixtures for brazing, glass sealing and other special secondary applications. While the latter uses may not be deemed to be of a critical nature, their value in expediting work is appreciable.

The major requirements of a ceramic material to serve in place of block talc have been listed as follows: [1]

1. The material must be sufficiently soft to be machinable with steel or carbide tools.

2. It must be uniform in texture to produce clean, sharp cuts.

3. It must have a low firing shrinkage to maintain accurate dimensions.

4. It must be nonfriable and strong after firing.

5. If used in a vacuum tube (as spacers in electronic tubes) it must degas easily and completely.

6. It must have good dielectric properties both at room and elevated temperatures.

7. It must be capable of being stored for a long period of time without harmful effects.

Here Are Some Materials

A. *Phosphate-Bonded Talc*—This discussion is based upon the investigations of Comeforo, Breedlove, and Thurnauer [1] which have shown that it is possible to form a consolidated block from powdered, domestic talc by the use of phosphates as a binder. The product obtained satisfies the requirements previously listed and, in addition, possesses several desirable characteristics which block talc lacks.

In brief, the fabrication techniques employed are those conventional for the manufacture of ceramic insulators by the dry-press method. The phosphate, preferably phosphoric acid, is blended with the ground talc and granulated prior to forming. The amount of acid used can be varied over an appreciable range, but 10% by weight of an 85% solution would be a representative value. The particle size of the talc is not critical, although specimens containing particles coarser than 40 mesh show a tendency for individual particles to break away, giving a rougher texture.

Dry-pressing is not the only method by which phosphate-bonded talc may be formed, as hydrostatic pressing and hot pressing techniques are also applicable.

All ceramic parts for the General Electric 7077 tube are formed on this Stokes automatic press. Balance at left is used for weight control of the part and the operator is ''milking'' a part for correct thickness.

The properties of dry-pressed phosphate-bonded talc are compared with block talc and other machinable ceramics in Table I.

The fact that phosphate-bonded talc can be fabricated by conventional ceramic techniques as well as machining is one of the most significant advantages it possess over natural block talc from which parts can only be machined, at a great waste of material.

Hot-Pressed Synthetic Mica

B. *Hot-Pressed Synthetic Mica*—This recently developed new ceramic type, a result of the research conducted by the U. S. Bureau of Mines synthetic mica program, and continued by the Brush Beryllium Co. represents the first ceramic that is readily machinable in its final form with steel or carbide tools. Intricate shapes may be machined from a block of hot-pressed synthetic mica to tolerances limited only by the ability of the machinist and his equipment. The problem of firing shrinkage is completely eliminated.

In addition to its machinability, hot-pressed synthetic mica is a good electrical insulator, chemically stable, has a smooth texture and its porosity can be varied from approximately 20% to vacuum tightness possibly suitable for use as envelopes or windows in microwave tubes.

Detailed descriptions of the processing technique, batch materials and compositions, and the physical, chemical and electrical properties of this material have been published elsewhere in the literature.[2]

A summary of the mechanical and electrical properties of hot-pressed synthetic mica is given in Table I. Another of the intriguing possibilities of this material is the fact that its composition can be varied over wide limits due to the extensive isomorphic substitutions possible in the mica structure. It is one of the advantages of synthetic minerals, and particularly of synthetic mica, that the composition can be "tailor made" to fit specific requirements. To exemplify the manner in which specific properties may be varied by appropriate changes in the synthetic mica composition, the properties of several different hot-pressed synthetic mica compositions, all of less than 0.5% water absorption, are compared in Table II.

Phosphate-Bonded Synthetic Mica

C. *Phosphate-Bonded Synthetic Mica*—The many unique features possessed by hot-pressed synthetic mica render it outstanding as a machinable ceramic dielectric requiring the ultimate dimensional control. As the hot-pressing technique is relatively expensive and the complexity of the product that can be fabricated directly is limited, research was started in 1951 to develop an inexpensive method of forming synthetic mica, preferably by use of the dry press process at a cost comparable to the more conventional ceramics.

Using the knowledge gained from prior research on the consolidation of talc by the use of phosphates as a bond,[1] Comeforo applied essentially the same procedures to a study of the phosphate-bonding of finely ground synthetic mica.[3] By using phosphoric acid as the bonding agent for powdered synthetic mica, a low-shrinkage, glass-free, machinable dielectric was obtained by dry pressing whose properties were controllable by varying the mica composition, the forming pressure, the firing temperature, and the phosphate content. The total shrinkage was easily maintained at less than 3% with the transverse strength in excess of 6000 lb. per sq. in. However, by this method a dense, impervious ceramic was not produced; the water absorption seldom was less than 4% when forming pressures of 10,000 lb. per sq. in. or less were employed. The range in the properties of synthetic fluor-mica bonded with 5–15% of orthophosphoric acid (85% solution) are presented in Table I.

TABLE II

Variation of properties by use of different hot-pressed synthetic mica compositions

Property	Mica composition	Property value
Specific Gravity (g/cc)	$KMg_3BSi_3O_{10}F_2$	2.75
	$BaMg_{2-1/2}AlSi_3O_{10}F_2$	3.39
Hardness	$KMg_3BSi_3O_{10}F_2$	.49 [a]
	$BaMg_{2-1/2}AlSi_3O_{10}F_2$	260 [a]
Thermal expansion		
(20–600° C.)	$KMg_3BSi_3O_{10}F_2$	12.6×10^{-6}
(cm/cm/° C.)	$BaMg_{2-1/2}AlSi_3O_{10}F_2$	7.9×10^{-6}
Poisson's ratio	$KMg_3BSi_3O_{10}F_2$	0.16
(stress of 10 tsi)	$KMg_3AlSi_3O_{10}F_2$	0.25
Power Factor	$KMg_3BSi_3O_{10}F_2$	0.0007
(1 mc)	$BaMg_3Al_2Si_2O_{10}F_2$	0.0003
Dielectric constant	$KMg_3BSi_3O_{10}F_2$	5.9
(1 mc)	$BaMg_3Al_2Si_2O_{10}F_2$	7.6

[a] Knoop number, 100 gm. load used.

There are additional ceramics besides those of the talc and synthetic mica types discussed that are sometimes referred to as machinable. To the writers' knowledge, all of these are machinable by virtue of the brittleness of the ceramic rather than softness. That is, the latter types are very porous thereby permitting a tool to chip, crush or pull out particles rather than cut through the ceramic grain. These may be considered machinable only in the same sense that insulating firebrick or foam glass is machinable and, therefore, are not discussed here.

Low Firing Shrinkage Ceramics

D. *Low Firing Shrinkage Ceramics*—By employing certain relatively unique forming processes as hot-pressing and fusion casting it is possible to circumvent shrinkage problems in the fabrication of some, usually simple, ceramic shapes. As these techniques are still largely confined to the laboratory in the ceramic industry, and as only a few ceramic types have been investigated, the present section will be confined to low shrinkage ceramic compositions as are produced by using more familiar dry-press, extrusion, casting and turning processes.

There is no firm demarcation to distinguish between a low- and high-shrinkage ceramic. If the specification prepared by the Munitions Board [4] for block talc is used, then a total shrinkage of 3% might properly be established as the upper limit for a low shrinkage ceramic.

Phosphate-bonded synthetic mica and phosphate-bonded talc, discussed in the previous sections as machinable ceramics, must also be regarded as low-firing shrinkage ceramics as their linear shrinkage is 3% or less. In fact, a zero-shrinkage composition was developed in which tetrasilicic fluormica ($KMg_{2-1/2}Si_4O_{10}F_2$) is bonded with phosphoric acid.[5]

Most ceramics are composed of a multiplicity of raw materials. Some impart sufficient workability to permit the fabrication of the body, others develop the desired chemical, physical and electrical properties over a definite temperature range, and frequently, some govern the color of the fired ceramic. This blending and compromising of properties constitutes the commercial ceramic compositions. They also greatly influence the firing shrinkage.

Foreman inspects a plaque of wax-mounted ceramic parts in the Blanchard grinder. Ceramic parts for the General Electric 7077 tube are ground to ±0.0003″ tolerances.

Porosity Always Present

Regardless of the forming technique employed, some voids or pores exist. The dehydration and decomposition of the components during firing further increase the porosity. As the firing process continues some components may melt or react to form a liquid phase which tends to fill the voids and to coalesce the particles. The combination of these factors results in fired shrinkages as high as 25% in some compositions.

One way to counteract this shrinkage is to incorporate a constituent into the ceramic composition which inverts permanently to a less dense, consequently larger volume, phase. The essential stipulation that such a material also possess the attributes required for a commercial ceramic greatly limits the choice. Since his work on the Li_2O-Al_2O_3-SiO_2 system,[6] Hatch has considered the use of the alpha-beta spodumene inversion as a means of achieving a low shrinkage ceramic.[7] In the inversion of alpha to beta spodumene a volume increase of approximately 30% occurs.

The extensive research conducted by Hummel [8] and associates on the lithia-alumina-silicate system with particular emphasis on various binary and ternary compositions has already resulted in the development of extremely low thermal expansion ceramics.[9] The knowledge gained from these studies is also helping to serve as a basis for low firing shrinkage ceramics, centered around the spodumene inversion or its devitrification from a glassy phase.

Zero Firing Shrinkage

Utilizing this information, the New Jersey Ceramic Experiment Station has undertaken the development of ceramic bodies of zero firing shrinkage.[10] Several compositions have achieved this objective. Bodies composed of spodumene and lead bisilicate, as typified by 60% spodumene and 40% lead bisilicate, undergo no shrinkage when pressed at 24–28 tons per sq. in. and fired to 2000° F. In addition to its exceptionally low shrinkage, this composition has a thermal expansion coefficient less than 3×10^{-6} in./in./°C.

Although a minor point at this time, the use of lead compounds in ceramic compositions designed primarily for electronic devices may place reservation on their applicability. For ceramic-to-metal assemblies in which the metallizing and brazing are performed in reducing atmospheres the tendency for the lead to reduce may render such ceramics ineffectual.

Research on zero shrinkage ceramics is in its initial stages, yet such compositions have already evolved. Now it can be hoped that such bodies will be developed that embody the high mechanical strength, excellent electrical characteristics and thermal stability now available in ceramics exhibiting higher firing shrinkages.

CHAPTER XVIII

SHAPING CERAMICS TO PRECISION TOLERANCES— PART 2

J. E. COMEFORO
Frenchtown Porcelain Co.

T. S. STANISLAW
Sylvania Electric Products, Inc.

For most applications, the more familiar, but high shrinkage, ceramics are specified. Aside from an established reputation, these ceramics have characteristics not yet available in the low shrinkage ceramics descirbed in the preceding section.

The generally quoted tolerance yardstick for these high shrinkage ceramics, namely $\pm 1\%$ with no tolerance less than ± 0.005 or ± 0.007, depending upon composition, is usually no longer applicable because of the increased demand for greater precision in ceramic components. Requests for tolerances within $\pm 0.002''$ are now common, and for some applications tolerances within $\pm 0.0005''$ are required. To make such tolerances a reality, rigid control, augmented by some good fortune, must be exercised over each component and operation.

Because the need for specially shaped ceramics begins during the design stages of a device embodying ceramics, samples are required for mechanical models and prototype assemblies before production can be justified. As these ceramics are usually not classified as production orders, it has become common to have a special department to make these parts.

This department has come to be known as a "model shop." This name is derived from the initial use to which these precision ceramics are put. Because the major reason the relatively precise tolerances can be met and maintained in the "model shop" is care in controlling each process, the name may be more appropriate if considered as a model which might be emulated for the production of all ceramics.

Details of Laboratory

To make the reader more familiar with the function and operation of a "model shop," a specific precision parts laboratory [11] will be discussed in detail. In this case, dry-pressing is considered; however, the same principles apply to other processes.

In the authors' opinion a "model shop" must do more than supply required parts. It must provide rapid and efficient service and also sound engineering design advice so that in the event parts reach the production stage they can be made as economically as required by the particular application involved.

It is rare for the first design to remain unchanged. Sometimes design changes are minor, at other times, major. Not only is it frustrating for the ceramic user to wait long periods to obtain revised versions of his original design, but valuable time is lost, time which costs a great deal of money and which may result in the unsuccessful fulfillment of a contract. The "model shop" must keep pace with these changing ideas lest they be lost before they are tried.

In the Sylvania Electric Products ceramic laboratory in Mineola, N. Y., going from a sketch to a finished, fired part in 10 days is not unusual and revisions to an existing design frequently can be made in five days.

An example will illustrate our concept of the rapid service possible. A Sylvania engineer from a distanct location telephoned a request for four different ceramic parts with delivery within two weeks. The parts, with dimensional tolerancesc which varied from a minimum of $\pm$ 0.001" to a maximum of $\pm$ 0.003", were described over the telephone and one week later several hundred pieces were shipped. To accomplish this four separate pressing molds were made and these parts pressed, fired and inspected within one week.

Pressing Die Consideration

E. *Pressing Dies*—The pressing dies are normally designed and made within the ceramic group. Die design is a routine matter and unless some unusual feature is encountered the die is made from the sketch of the ceramic or from rough die sketches. Frequently the same technician makes the die and presses at least the first few samples.

This "break-in" period establishes how the die is functioning and whether modifications or changes are required. Since this same person may also prepare the batches and fire and inspect the ceramics, he has an appreciation of the entire fabrication process and knows from practical experience how each step is dependent upon the other and in general how variations from a set procedure will affect the final product. This procedure may not be possible in all organizations, but it has the desirable merits of simplicity and efficiency.

Often for small lots, dies used in conjunction with manually operated hydraulic presses are made from cold rolled steel of SAE 1010 or 1020 grade. Pins to form small holes are made from piano wire or drill rod. The number of pieces that can be pressed from such die before overhauling or rebuilding is necessary depends upon the nature of the body being pressed, the geometry of the part and the tolerances required. Bodies of greater than 95% alumina have been pressed dense successfully in cold rolled dies without undue difficulty. It is obvious that the relatively soft steatites and similar compositions cause less die wear and, therefore, minimize die maintenance.

Extensive Pressing Possible

It can safely be stated that pressing several hundred parts with these dies is possible. Normally a large number of pieces is not required from dies made of soft steel but occasions have arisen where the uncertainties of a program and the ecenomics involved dictated such action. It should be pointed out that with these somewhat simplified dies there may occur problems of die fill uniformity and alignment both during the pressing and ejection cycles which are greatly influenced by the operator.

Parts requiring thin walls or ''deep drawing'' present the greatest difficulty as the abrasive ceramic grains which get between moving parts may cause galling and tearing of the metal surfaces during pressing.

A die for pressing a part of very complex geometry has small holes, external projections and abrupt changes in cross sectional thickness.

Hardened tool steel dies sometimes are used in conjunction with the manually operated presses and always with the automatic ones since good alignment of the latter permits using closer fits between moving die parts and many more parts are expected of the ordinary tool steels which are required to be made with them. In place of using costly grinding after hardening to a Rockwell ''C'' or 55 to 60, air hardening steels which do not require this finishing step have been used with good success.

If scaling during hardening occurs it is so thin as to require nothing more than a very light polish, and as a matter of fact, quite frequently this step can be eliminated as the dies polish themselves during use.

Pressing Important Factor

F. *Die Design Considerations*—The nature of the finished ceramic part is greatly influenced by the way it is pressed. Clearances between moving die parts are different for the soft steel dies used with the manually operated presses and the hardened ones used on the mechanical presses. For the former 0.00075″ to 0.001″ has been found satisfactory and for the latter approximately half this much. The die must be designed to obtain maximum flow of the dried powders under pressure and the various moving parts must move in the proper sequence if difficulties are to be avoided. A high polish on die parts in contact with the powders is very important.

The die requirements for several ceramic shapes will indicate some of the problems encountered. If a flat disc is considered, the essential die parts consist of three components, a barrel of appropriate diameter and two punches. Thickness of the pressed part will be dependent upon the amount of die fill, other factors being equal. If pressure is applied only by one moving punch, the fired disc will possibly be warped and distorted because of unequal pressed density, the extent of the distortion being more severe the thicker the part. Conversely, if both punches are permitted to move toward one another simultaneously and at about the same rate, distortion will be minimized. Die fill should be as uniform as possible; this factor assumes greater importance the thinner the disc. Obviously, a disc is the simplest shape encountered.

Increase in Complexity

As the geometry of a part becomes more complex so does the pressing operation since ceramic powders under pressure do not behave as fluids but offer resistance to flow because of friction between the particles of a mixture and between the particles and the various die parts.

Abrupt changes of cross section are undesirable and cause many problems. An illustration of such a part is a cup; the greater the ratio between the depth of its sidewall and its bottom thickness the more difficult it is to form. A cup having this ratio of 8 to 1 and a powder with a compaction ratio of 2½ to 1 will be considered. The latter factor is merely the ratio of the height of unpressed powder (die fill) to the height of pressed powder. If the punch which forms the inside contour and the open end of the sidewall were one, the bottom would be pressed hard and the sidewall practically not at all since the sidewall forming punch ideally should be allowed to move approximately 8 times the distance the other punch moves and actually has moved only the same distance. To minimize this variation in density, two independent pressing actions are necessary, one on the closed end, the other on the cylindrical portion of the sidewall.

A Complicating Factor

An additional factor which complicates matters is the sequence with which the punches move. The sidewall forming or "bottom" punch cannot be allowed to move too fast or too soon, otherwise powder will be forced into the closed end and make it thicker than desired. This condition can be exaggerated to such an extent that a very shallow cup with thick bottom results or under a less severe condition excess powder can be forced into the radius at the junction of the sidewall and bottom and thus cause cracking in this area.

A not unusual condition to find in deep cups is "bowing" or "hourglassing" of the sidewalls, caused primarily by lower pressed density in their center area. Pressing friction and nonuniform die fill are responsible for this distortion. The die fill problem becomes greater the greater its depth and the thinner the wall of the cup.

Preparation of Batches

G. *Batch Preparation*—The physical preparation of ceramic batches is very important and must be done under carefully controlled and reproducible conditions to assure physical and chemical homogeneity and reproducibility from batch to batch. The properties of the prepared batch have a profound influence on die fill and on pressing characteristics and may even influence die life. Care is taken in the selection of raw materials with particular emphasis on purity and particle size. It is vital that the properties remain constant from shipment to shipment. The general steps of weighing batch constituents, mixing and grinding, drying, pulverizing, granulating and screening are as follows:

Batch materials are weighed on scales of several kilograms capacity and when deemed necessary a 3-kilogram capacity chainomatic balance with an accuracy of 5 milligrams is used. The weighed materials and necessary milling water are charged into porcelain-lined pebble mills with the required volume of pebbles; mixing and grinding thus are accomplished simultaneously. Temporary binders and lubricants are added with the mill charge. Wax in water emulsions and magnesium stearate have been found an ideal combination. That wax emulsion must be selected which does not break down during the milling operations.

Milling Time Varies

Milling time varies with each particular composition and is determined experimentally by trial and error; that time is selected which gives the densest body consistent with good pressing characteristics. Milling times range from 4 to 48 hours, depending on the batch composition. Total contamination from the ceramic mill and pebbles, as well as from impurities in the raw materials, has rarely been found to exceed 0.5% for the high alumina compositions developed by Sylvania.

With the particular combination of binder and lubricant mentioned, drying is a step which must be carefully controlled. It is accomplished in a recirculating air shelf dryer; the milled slip is held in shallow aluminum pans of the maximum area the dryer can accommodate. Slip depth does not exceed 1 inch. During the drying cycle, two heat stages are used: The

Dual purpose pulverizer and granulating mill used in preparation of body for dry pressing.

first relatively low and for the purpose of evaporating the water; the second held for a short duration exceeds the melting point of the wax and thereby causes it to coat the dried powder.

Second Heating Step Essential

If this second heating step is not used the mix is fluffy and light, does not granulate properly and consequently contains too many "fines," which cause such troubles as laminations in the pressed pieces; die galling and sticking, and too large a compaction ratio. Too high a drying temperature causes decomposition of the organic additives and, depending upon the severity of the decomposition, causes discoloration of the mix and loss of necessary lubricating and bonding qualities.

The dried "cake" is puverized in a variable speed, stainless steel-lined hammer mill type comminuting machine which also is used for forming the pressing granules by the simple expedient of reversing the comminuting chamber and changing screens. Reversing the chamber causes the powder to be struck by knife-edges rather than by the flatfaced impact faces of the blades.

To the pulverized powder an experimentally determined percentage of water is added so that pressing granules can be formed. For the small batches this water may be kneaded into the mix by hand. This method, however, is not entirely satisfactory because of the loss of water by evaporation and the difficulty of obtaining uniform distribution of the water throughout the mixture.

More satisfactory methods utilize rather a muller-type mixer, preferably made of stainless steel to avoid iron contamination resulting from rusting of the iron parts in contact with the mix; a twin shell blender, or a vertical paddle-type mixer. Care must be taken to avoid batch contamination, loss of water by evaporation and non-uniform distribution of the water. The moistened mixture is granulated as mentioned above and the granules thus formed dried.

Separating Dried Granules

Separation of the dried granules is accomplished on mechanical, reciprocating cloth screens which are hopper fed. The particular equipment used gives three screen fractions plus oversize and fines on each pass. Often it is desirable to minimize fines which adhere to the various screen fractions; this is accomplished by slow feed and several passes over the screens. The particular screen fractions desired depend upon the parts to be formed.

As a very general guide, that granule fraction is used which has a maximum dimension of one-third the minimum clearance found between die parts which form the contour of the piece. This ratio minimizes "bridging" of the granules during die fill. Too coarse granules do not crush completely and bond together and their outlines are readily visible on the pressed and fired specimen. Too fine granules result in excessive compaction ratios and pressing friction.

Granule hardness is another factor which should be controlled as too hard or too soft granules will have the same effect as too coarse or too fine ones. Other factors being equal, hardness is a function of the amount of granulating water added; the smaller the percentage added, the softer the granules. This property is also influenced by the amount and character of binders used and the drying process.

Pressing Procedure

H. *Pressing Procedure*—In the prior discussion on die design, some mention was made of the pressing operation. This step certainly is not so simple as it appears to one watching a press turn out parts at a rapid rate without apparent difficulty. It is made possible by the control of the batch preparation, dies design and pressing technique. Die fill must be uniform and consistent; it depends upon free-flowing granules, the rate at which the fill cup moves over the die cavity, the manner in which it scrapes across the die surface and die design.

The speed of the punches entering the die cavity and the clearances between moving die parts determine how well air will be expelled from among the granules. If this speed is too rapid, air will be trapped within the die and the well-known pressing laminations will result, either immediately or during the firing cycle. Pressing speed must be experimentally determined and differs for different compositions and parts which involve different geometry.

Nonplastic bodies should be pressed slowly as should those which for some reason or other have had lubricants kept to a minimum.

The importance of the proper sequence of the movements of die parts has been previously discussed.

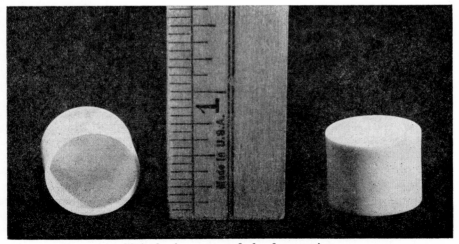

92% alumina cups made by dry pressing.

Pressure Time Varies

The length of time that pressure is applied again is dependent upon composition and shape of the part under consideration. As a general rule too long a dwell is not harmful except from the economic point of view. The optimum pressing pressure to use normally is determined when a specific composition initially is developed; the lowest pressure consistent with adequate density and pressed strength should be used. This will minimize die wear and pressing laminations. Pressures in the range of 6,000 to 10,000 psi have been found adequate. Higher pressures may result in higher pressed densities but the increase is disproportionate to the increase in pressure necessary.

If it becomes mandatory to alter slightly the final dimensions of a ceramic shape made from an existing mold, such as occasioned by die wear after extended use, or by a minor miscalculation of the firing shrinkage, it is often possible to accomplish this correction by making the appropriate change in forming pressure. The dimensional change required must be small, otherwise large changes in the forming pressure will alter the properties of the ceramic.

Firing in Electric Kilns

I. *Firing*—Firing is accomplished in electric kilns utilizing nonmetallic heating elements up to 1350° C.; for higher temperatures gas-air fired kilns are used. Commercial kilns are available which cover most applications. It is well to take precautions to heat slowly during the initial stages of firing to protect both the furnace refractories and the parts being fired and to duplicate firing schedules closely once they are established.

Excellent control equipment is available and should be utilized; program controllers remove much of the guesswork from this operation. For periodic kilns the natural cooling cycle normally is adequate and therefore once the source of heat is shut off there is little to do but wait.

After a part has been fired it is important to evaluate it in relationship to its intended application. Physical dimensions can be obtained with generally available measuring tools and electrical and physical properties determined by published methods such as those distributed by A.S.T.M.

Special Grinding and Shaping

There have always been applications of ceramics which require tolerances closer than the standard plus or minus 1%. However, until the demands of the electronic industry, whose needs greatly grew in urgency and size during Worfld War II, made prompt and decisive action mandatory, the grinding of fired ceramics was largely confined to the salvaging of oversize or warped parts. Even then such grinding was reserved for special shapes.

The impetus of the war forced a change in this philosophy. With the cooperation of the grinding wheel and equipment manufacturers, techniques were established to grind the hard, brittle, low heat conductive ceramics to tolerances of ± 0.0001″.

J. *Grinding and Drilling Ceramics*—Now various types of disc, centerless and universal grinders and lapping machines are an integral part of the production facilities of many ceramic companies. Such equipment is discussed and illustrated by Williams.[13] With the use of such grinding equipment, ceramics may be ground to tolerances of 0.0001″ in flatness and 0.0005″ parallelism. Likewise the internal and external diameters and concentricity of cylinders may be rigidly maintained. Spheres up to 4″ in diameter are also being diamond ground to ± 0.0005″ sphericity. With the use of this grinding equipment, however, it is not possible to control the diameter of holes appreciably less than 0.20″ nor their locations.

Diamond Drills Often Used

When precisely dimensioned small holes and certain ceramics symmetrically shaped about an axis are required, diamond drills and tools mounted in lathes or end mills are often used. There are various gem and optical supply companies that cater to the machining of such ceramic parts. Tolerances of ± 0.001″ are attainable with delivery usually within three weeks' time.

The machining cost per piece is comparatively high and for production quantities usually prohibitive, except in very limited applications. For developmental purposes, the use of such relatively expensive tools in conjunction with readily available machine shop equipment enables ceramic users to make their own shapes without the delay inherent in obtaining the few samples required from a ceramic manufacturer.

K. *Ultrasonic Drilling*—Largely within the past five years, a new method of cutting or drilling ceramics has become commercially available. This is the ultrasonic machine tool which uses a magnetostrictive transducer to impart rapid particle acceleration to abrasive powders suspended in a liquid, usually water, between the vibrating tool and the ceramic. A recent discussion of the applicability of this process to ceramics and allied materials has been given by Hartley.[14]

The frequency commonly used for cutting ceramics is 20–30 kc. The rate of material removal is dependent upon the amplitude of the tool, the size and type of abrasive and the composition of the tool tip and the ceramic.

Produce Almost Any Shape

It has been generally established that it is possible to produce almost any shape by ultrasonic grinding. Shapes that are virtually impossible to form in ceramics by diamond tools or grinding techniques can be readily made by ultrasonics.

The reason for this is that the tool used in ultrasonics does not actually perform the cuttings; in fact, it does not directly contact the ceramic. The tool is made as the male counterpart of the desired shape. At it does not do the grinding, it may be made of cold rolled and unhardened tool steel. Brass and copper tubing have been used by the authors in drilling small holes.

Although some of the commercial units are complete and their operation rather straightforward, a skilled machinist is necessary to produce ceramic shapes to the tolerance for which the unit is purchased. In addition to possessing the skill required to manipulate a machine tool so as to achieve tolerance of ± 0.001″, for best results the operator should also make the necessary tools and braze them onto the transmitting cone. Furthermore, personal judgment is an important factor, e.g., in minimizing such difficulties as the wandering of small holes and side lapping during drilling.

Limits of Ultrasonic Machining

There are certain limits to ultrasonic machining of ceramics that may be mentioned. The size of the tool that can be used is limited. As an indication, the maximum size disc that can be removed from a larger ceramic in one operation is approximately 1½″ in diameter. This size will increase as the ultrasonic machine tools become more powerful. The minimum diameter hole that can be drilled is approximately 0.015″, and to achieve a straight, vertical hole requires care, as mentioned earlier.

Tool wear varies with the tool composition, the abrasive type, and the ceramic, but seldom can the ratio of depth of cut to tool wear be expected to exceed 20/1. With small holes in dense alumina, 5/1 or less has been observed. This means frequent tool change and delay.

The depth of the hole that can be drilled decreases with the hole diameter, but with an 0.10″ diameter as our example, the maximum depth would be approximately 0.75″. For counterbored holes, a second drilling operation is required.

The ultrasonic machining of ceramics is not a fast process. However, for a small number of special shapes it is finding definite use. In addition to its use in making precision ceramics, ultrasonic machine tools are finding application in ceramic laboratories for machining carbide dies for extrusion and dry pressing molds.

Summary

This report has reviewed the studies made during and especially since World War II in the development of attaining precise ceramic shapes. Where tolerances of ± 0.001″ were once regarded as unfeasible, several means of satisfying such tolerances are now available to the ceramic industry. These have been classified under new ceramic types, embodying machinable and low shrinkage ceramics; new techniques, describing the manner by which any ceramic composition regardless of the magnitude of its firing shrinkage may be dimensionally controlled, and special grinding and shaping techniques, which discusses the grinding and machining of ceramics with diamond tools and wheel and by ultrasonics.

REFERENCES

1. Comeforo, J. E., Breedlove, J. G., Thurnauer, Hans, ''Phosphate-Bonded Talc: A Superior Block-Talc Substitute,'' Jour. Amer. Ceram. Soc., 37 (4) 191–95 (1954).

2. a. Comeforo, J. E., Hatch, R. A., Humphrey, R. A., and Eitel, Wilhelm, ''Synthetic Mica Investigations, I: A Hot-Pressed Machinable Ceramic Dielectric,'' ibid., 36, 286–94 (1953).

    b. Eitel, Wilhelm, Hatch, R. A., and Denny, M. V., ''Synthetic Mica Investigations, II: The Role of Fluorides in Mica Batch Reactions,'' ibid., 36, 341–48 (1953).

3. Comeforo, J. E., ''Synthetic Mica Investigations, V: A Low-Shrinkage Machinable Ceramic of Phosphate-Bonded Synthetic Mica,'' ibid., 37, 427–432 (1954).

4. National Stockpile Specification P-53a, Material Purchase Specifications. Talc Lump, General Services Administration, Emergency Procurement Service, Sept. 7, 1950.

5. Comeforo, J. E., ''Machinable Ceramic and Process of Manufacture,'' U. S. Patent 2,704,261, March 15, 1955.

6. Hatch, R. A., ''Phase Equilibrium in the System Li_2O-Al_2O_3-SiO_2, Amer. Mineral, 28, 471–96 (1943).

7. Personal Communications.

8. a. Hummel, F. A., ''Thermal Expansion Properties of Natural Lithia Minerals,'' Foote Prints, 20 (2), 3–11 (1948).

    b. Hummel, F. A., ''Thermal Expansion Properties of Some Synthetic Lithia Minerals,'' Jour. Amer. Ceram. Soc., 34, 235–39 (1951).

9. Hummel, F. A., ''Ceramics for Thermal Shock Resistance,'' Ceramic Industry, 65 (11), 73–75 (1955).

10. Signal Corps Research Program, Contract No. DA-36-039-sc-42577, from December 1, 1952 to December 1, 1954. Also Contract No. DA-36-039-sc-64566.

11. Sylvania Electric Products, Inc., Ceramic Laboratory, Mineola, L. I., N. Y.

12. Stainislaw, T. S., ''Model Shop for Dry Pressing Precision Ceramics,'' Ceramic Age, 1954.

13. Williams, Robert, ''Ceramics for Vacuum Tube Envelopes,'' ibid., 1954.

14. Hartley, M. S., ''Ultrasonic Machining of Brittle Materials,'' Electronics, 132–135, (1), 1956.

CHAPTER XIX

HIGH DIELECTRIC CONSTANT CERAMICS

J. W. DEADERICK*

American Lava Corp.

As an introduction to the subject of high dielectric constant ceramics it is appropriate first to consider the historical background of electrical insulating materials relevant to the development of a definition of the term "dielectric constant" and its significance in electrical circuits.

Ceramic dielectrics, namely glass and porcelain, were used by experimenters in the early part of the 18th Century while investigating the nature of the phenomenon now known as the electrostatic charge. The more commonly used insulating substances during the course of these experiments were amber, rubber, resin, sulphur, sealing wax and shellac.

The Leyden jar, one of the earliest devices for the storage of a quantity of electricity, used glass, a ceramic material, as the dielectric. It was noted that following a spark discharge of a Leyden jar, a number of sucessive discharges of decreasing magnitude could be obtained. This phenomenon was explained as the absorption of electricity within the dielectric material during the charging cycle followed by a gradual escape of the electrical charge from the dielectric medium.

Faraday's Contribution

Michael Faraday was the first investigator to publish a systematic study of the dielectric materials used in electrical condensers. He found that electrical condensers having identical insulator configurations, but containing different dielectric materials, had varying charge storage or inductive capacities. For instance, a condenser having sulphur as the dielectric had an inductive capacity which was approximately twice that of a similar condenser having air as the dielectric. The term "specific inductive capacity" therefore became the predecessor of the synonymous terms "permittivity" and "dielectric constant" used in today's literature.

Coulomb's Law

In 1785 Coulomb developed his law of electric force which states that the force between two electric charges varies inversely as the square of their distance apart, and directly as the product of the two electric charges. Coulomb found that it was necessary to apply a constant factor in his

---

* Deceased.

equation to compensate for the variation of the force between electric charges when different material media replaced a vacuum. The value of this factor "K" was unity for vacuum and compared with 1.000594 for air. For all practical purposes, however, this difference is so small that the value for air may be assumed as unity.

The electrostatic unit of capacity is defined as the capacity of a conductor such that one electrostatic unit of charge raises its potential by one electrostatic unit of potential, or $C = Q/V$, where

Q is the charge

V is the amount of potential rise

C is the electrostatic unit of capacity.

Using the coulomb and the volt as units of quantity and potential, the unit of electrical capacity is defined as the farad, which is the capacity of a conductor requiring a coulomb to raise its potential by one volt. Since one coulomb equals 3×10^9 electrostatic units, and one volt equals $\frac{1}{3} \times 10^{-2}$ electrostatic units, one farad becomes 9×10^{11} electrostatic units of capacity. This value is so large as to be cumbersome, and it has become practical to use the microfarad, 9×10^5 electrostatic units, or one-millionth of a farad, for the common unit of capacity.

Some Representative Formulas

For an isolated sphere of radius r, the electrostatic capacity C equals a constant multiplied by the radius, or

$$C = Kr$$

where K is practically unity if the sphere is suspended in air. For a sphere of radius r surrounded by a concentric spherical shell of radius R,

$$C = K\frac{Rr}{R\text{-}r}$$

A pair of parallel conductor plates may be considered as parts of two very large concentric spheres. By taking into consideration the factors given above we can now arrive at the basic formula for electrical capacity in electrostatic units which is

$$C = K\frac{A}{4\pi d}$$

where A is the area of one of a pair of equal parallel conducting plates

d is the relatively small distance between the plates

K is the dielectric constant of the insulating medium between the plates.

By use of the proper conversion and correction factors the dielectric constants of various insulating media can be calculated from measurements of the electrical capacity and the size and spacing of the conductor plates.

Values Less Than 10

Most of the commonly used solid electrical insulating materials have values of dielectric constant less than 10. In the early part of the 20th Century German scientists discovered that titanium dioxide ceramics exhibited a considerably higher value of dielectric constant than had been encountered previously in other well known ceramics such as glass and electrical porcelain. Up to that time paper and mica were the chief dielectric materials used in the manufacture of electrical capacitors. Having no domestic source of mica, Europe was faced with a critical mica shortage prior to and during World War I which gave emphasis to the extensive search for suitable replacements.

Titanium dioxide with clay additions constituted the early high dielectric constant ceramic materials. Having dielectric constants of about 60, ceramic materials for use in high voltage and other applications were successfully developed in the early 1930's, but the units were bulky in spite of a dielectric constant of approximately 10 times that of electrical porcelain and glass.

By 1933 quantities of ecramic dielectric capacitors were being used on the Continent and in Great Britain by the radio and electronic industries with considerable improvement in control of the materials during manufacture and stability in service. These units were limited to temperature compensating and general purpose use.

Titanium Dioxide Ceramics

In 1935 titanate ceramics were being investigated in the United States chiefly for general purpose and temperature compensating capacitor applications. It had been found that titanium dioxide ceramics could have their dielectric properties modified considerably by certain additions to the ceramic formula. Additions of magnesium oxide to titanium dioxide established a series of ceramics having temperature coefficients of dielectric constant varying from negative to positive, the dielectric constants ranging from about 15 to 95.

In about 1940 discovery of the unusual properties of the compound barium titanate gave rise to the expanding family of high dielectric constant ceramics having dielectric constants of from about 1200 for barium titanate to values as high as 10,000 for special ceramics having well defined and controllable electrical and physical characterisics.

Basic compositions consisted of major percentages of barium titanate with minor additions of alkaline earth titanates, zirconates and stannates. A very large number of compounds effective in modifying the electrical properties of barium titanate have been used over the past 15 years. These compounds have been classed as "peak shifters and/or peak flatteners" in relation to their effect upon the Curie point in the dielectric constant-temperature relationship in barium titanate ceramics.[1] The microstructure of these ceramics is complex, consisting of mixed crystal systems, solid solutions, or both, depending upon composition and heat treatment. The theoretical aspects of their dielectric behavior are not well understood but many papers on the subject have appeared in the literature, especially concerning the mechanism of ferroelectricity. The Laboratory for Insulation Research, Massachusetts Institute of Technology, has contributed greatly to the physics background.[2]

Produced in Many Sizes, Shapes

By careful control of the starting materials and manufacturing processes high dielectric constant ceramics are produced today in a host of sizes and shapes with great variety of built-in electrical properties. Of paramount importance is the control of the value of dielectric constant over a wide temperature range while maintaining low dielectric loss properties.

Extensive research and development work by institutional laboratories and manufacturers continues in an effort to improve dielectric constant-temperature relationships, to lower dielectric losses, to minimize loss of dielectric constant due to aging, to increase the resistance to dielectric breakdown at high temperatures and high voltages, and to reduce voltage sensitivity of dielectric constant among other properties of lesser importance for capacitor applications. The unusual characteristics of these ceramics offer many opportunities for their use in other applications such as dielectric amplifiers and electro-mechanical transducers.

Research with Other Materials

Research effort is being applied to other high dielectric constant ceramic materials such niobates, tantalates and zirconates in the search for high dielectric constant ceramic materials for withstanding higher operating temperatures and nuclear irradiation without degradation of the important electrical and physical characteristics. This has become a fertile field for research by both the ceramist and the theoretical physicist.

REFERENCES

1. Coffeen, W. W., Communications and Electronics (9) 704,709 (1953).
2. Hippel, A. von, Ferroelectricity, Domain Structure, and Phase Transitions of Barium Titanate, Reviews of Modern Physics, 22 (3) 221–237 (1950).

CHAPTER XX

HOW HIGH DIELECTRIC CONSTANT CERAMICS ARE MADE

JAMES G. BREEDLOVE

American Lava Corp.

Ceramic dielectrics for capacitors may be formed by any process used to form other ceramic materials. For reasons of over-all economy, only extrusion and dry pressing methods are used extensively. The conditions of large electrode area, minimum thickness of satisfactory physical strength and low cost of ceramic and of processing ceramics into capacitors are most satisfactorily obtained with simple tubes, discs and plates.

In the early years of ceramic dielectrics, tubular parts were more widely used than discs. Pressed parts have found increasing favor, however, and now make up a majority of the ceramic capacitor market.

Smaller quantities of dielectrics are produced by thin sheet methods and by slip casting. Other methods are used occasionally for special purposes.

Wet Milling Initial Step

Regardless of the forming method to be used, the initial step of processing is wet milling. Other mixing methods have generally failed to produce the uniformity required of ceramic dielectrics. The ball mills are usually lined with burrstone, and flint pebbles are employed as the mixing medium.

Removal of the water may be accomplished by centrifuging, filtering or by spray drying. The first two are generally employed for small or medium quantities of a variety of compositions. Spray drying is usually preferred when large quantities of relatively few compositions are to be processed. Organic binders are usually added to the ball mill when the material is to be spray dried. Binder has the effect of minimizing the number of ultrafine particles formed, which facilitates removal of the product from the air stream.

The dried material is prepared for extrusion by addition of binders, waxes, lubricants and water. The mixture is thoroughly mixed in a muller-type mixer. The extrusion itself may be accomplished with a pug-mill, but is usually done with an extrusion press. In any case thorough de-airing must be accomplished. After drying the extruded sticks are cut to the desired length before firing.

Granulating Follows Milling

After the ball milling operation, material to be dry pressed is first granulated to obtain the proper particle-size distribution. The individual grains must be compacted and should contain sufficient binder to give strength to the pressed part. Excess binder must be avoided since the

110

granules may be too hard to break down properly in the pressing operation which follows.

Muller-type mixers are preferred for the granulation of pressing material. The batch is prepared wet enough so that no excessively fine material will be present in the mixed batch. The oversize material may be broken down by passing through a slow speed hammer mill.

Granulating may also be accomplished in the spray drying operation. Excellent particle-size distributions are readily achieved by spray drying— but at a considerable sacrifice of grain density.

Press Selection Open

Almost any type of press may be used for dry pressing ceramic dielectrics. Sintered carbide dies are preferred. Small amounts of water and lubricants are added to the granulated material to temper the material, assist in grain breakdown and prevent sticking of the material to the punches. Material having high binder content and tightly compacted grains is pressed harder than softer material of low grain density. Hard-pressed discs and plates are considerably stronger and easier to handle. High tonnage mechanical or hydraulic presses are better suited for hard materials, and rotary presses are used to advantage in pressing softer materials.

Thin-sheet ceramic dielectrics are prepared by depositing a film of

At the silver painting department of Centralab Division of Globe-Union, Inc., Milwaukee, Wis., silver electrodes are applied to ceramic base plates.

ceramic material on a moving belt.* The slip is prepared by suitable additions of binder, plasticizer and solvent to the dry ceramic materials. After drying, the thin ceramic is stripped from the belt and stamped or cut to size.

The slip casting process is used primarily for high voltage capacitors where quality of internal structure is of prime importance or where the shape is more easily made by the casting process.

Firing of ceramic dielectrics is usually done in electric kilns. Reaction products from the combustion of fuels are generally harmful to the electrical qualities of ceramic dielectrics. Even where full muffles are tightly installed, the electrical qualities are often impaired.

Zirconium Oxide As Setter Material

Zirconium oxide is almost universally used as the setter material for high dielectric constant ceramic dielectrics. A few of the lower dielectric constant materials may be fired on zircon, alumina or other refractories. The zirconia setters are comparatively expensive, and represent a considerable part of the cost of ceramic dielectrics.

Firing cycles are short as compared to other ceramic materials. Four hours to 24 hours total firing cycle is common practice. Firing temperatures are in the range of 1100° C. to 1450° C. Materials of highest dielectric constant are generally fired at the highest temperatures and longest firing cycles.

----

* ''Fabrication of Thin Ceramic Sheets for Capacitors,'' G. N. Howatt *et al.*, Journal of the American Ceramic Society, 30 (8) 237–41 (1947).

CHAPTER XXI

USES OF HIGH DIELECTRIC CONSTANT CERAMICS

HARRY G. PRUETT, JR.

Radio Kemetal Industries, Inc.

Modern ceramic capacitors use a wide range of insulating material that often have unique characteristics. They are made in a wide range of temperature coefficients, and others have very high dielectric constants. They possess characteristics that are compatible for the modern electronic designer.

The Class I ceramic capacitor, or temperature compensating capacitor, may be obtained in a variety of either positive or negative temperature coefficeints. The temperature coefficient of capacitance is a measure of the capacitance change per unit capacitance per degree of temperature change with which the capacitor is associated. The unit commonly used for ceramic dielectric temperature coefficient measurement is parts per million per degree centigrade change (ppm/° C.).

Class I Applications

Class I ceramic dielectrics are well suited for applications where stability of capacitance characteristics is essential. The temperature coefficient of capacity of these ceramic materials is a function of the crystalline structure and can be determined for a number of ceramic compositions. Capacitance-temperature characteristics ranging from +100 ppm/° C. to −5600 ppm/° C. are available. By controlling the temperature coefficient of capacity, it is possible to use these ceramic capacitors to compensate for temperature variations in resonant circuits. Although temperature compensating capacitance is their primary importance, these same units may also be used for general purpose capacitors when uniformity and low losses are essential.

The positive temperature coefficient of capacitance of ceramic dielectrics range from +100 ppm/° C. to 0 ppm/° C., and have dielectric constant values from 6 to 30. The more popular temperature compensating ceramic capacitors are the negative temperature coefficient of capacitance. The negative temperature coefficient values range from 0 ppm/° C. to −5600 ppm/° C. The capacitors are currently available in capacitance values from .3 to 3,000 mmf. The dielectric constants range in value from 19 to 800.

Keep Losses at Minimum

In most tuned circuits that are temperature compensated, it is required that losses such as power factor be kept at a minimum. In an ideal capacitor, the conductors, or plates, would have zero resistance, and the dielectric would have infinite resistivity. When an alternating voltage is applied to such a capacitor, current will flow into the capacitor as the voltage is increasing and flow out as the voltage is decreasing. At the moment when the voltage is a maximum, no current will be flowing, and when the voltage is zero, the current will be a maximum. Hence, in a perfect capacitor, the current and voltage are 90° out of phase.

In actual capacitors the conditions as to the resistance in the plate and dielectric are not fulfilled and, in consequence, an alternating current flowing in a capacitor is not exactly 90° out of phase with the impressed voltage. The difference between 90° and the actual phase angle is called the ''phase difference.''

The Ideal Capacitor

In an ideal capacitor, there would be no consumption of power; the existence of a phase difference means a power loss, which manifests itself as an increase in temperature of the capacitor. The amount of the power loss is given, as for any part of a circuit, by $P = EI \cos \Theta$. The Θ is the phase angle between current and voltage, and the cosine Θ is the power factor.

In Class I dielectrics, power factor is expressed in terms of Q. A conventional expression for the magnitude of Q can be derived from the basic

The ultrasonic device shown here makes use of a barium titanate transducer.

concept of energy stored as compared to the energy dissipated per cycle in a resonant system. It is used as a measure of power factor and the relationship to its phase angle. Q is a figure of merit, usually associated with Class I or temperature compensating capacitors that can be compared to power factor in the high K "general purpose" Class II ceramic dielectrics.

'General Purpose' Units

The Class II, or "general purpose" ceramic capacitor, is the high K ceramic dielectric which has been developed to yield high capacitance in a minimum of space. Many high K ceramic dielectrics have been developed to permit a choice of various temperature operating limits. As the temperature-capacitance curve is not linear, these units are not used for temperature compensating as the Class I dielectrics. These units are designed for use as coupling and by-passing frequencies from the audio range to the ultra high radio frequencies. As the shape of the capacitor at high frequencies is important, ceramic capacitors are used extensively in the radio frequency range.

Class II Materials Constants

Dielectric constants for Class II materials range from 250 to 10,000, depending upon material constituents. The dielectric constant variations with respect to temperature may be controlled from a very low to a high percentage of change over large temperature ranges.

All ceramic capacitors are available in many sizes and shapes. This feature enables the capacitor to be used in devices that could not accommodate conventional types.

The ceramic capacitors are stable with age and the aging characteristics may be predetermined over long periods of time.

All of these facts show that there is a definite need for ceramic capacitors in the electronic industry. It is recognized as a superior type of dielectric material with electrical values that can be controlled and reproduced.

CHAPTER XXII

SOFT SOLDERING IN TECHNICAL CERAMICS

C. ALAN LINDQUIST, JR.

Astatic Corp.

Many technical ceramic components use fired-on silver electrodes to which are attached leads or other metallic devices by means of soft solders. Ceramic capacitors, printed circuits and piezoelectric transducers are well known examples of electronic components using such electrodes. In each case the soldering operation is an important step in fabrication and one that must be performed economically.

Solders Available

Soft soldering is done with alloys that melt below 700° F. About 30 common soft solders are available, but the ones generally used on ceramic components approximate the tin-lead eutectic composition (63% tin, 37% lead).

Eutectic solder has several advantages for our purposes. Solderability is directly related to wetting ability, and the eutectic alloy seems to wet best. Aside from that, it melts fastest and sets fastest which is of decided advantage when soldering thin films of silver on ceramic bodies. Molten solder has a tendency to leach away silver, causing what is known as "electrode scavenging." Hence, the longer the silver is in contact with solder, the greater the amount of scavenging.

An alloy containing a small percentage of silver is frequently selected as it also tends to prevent leaching of the electrode silver content. A 62% tin—36% lead—2% silver composition has attached leads to literally millions of ceramic capacitors. Actually, the tin-lead-silver eutectic occurs at 62.5—36.1—1.4.

Solder may be stocked in a number of forms. Usually bar solder is used for dipping baths and wire solder with copper bit "irons." The wire comes in several diameters, with or without a flux core. Preforms, in the shape of discs, washers, pellets, rings, etc., may be obtained for special jobs and where oven soldering is desired.

Selection of A Flux

The choice of flux is extremely important. Aside from removing oxide films and aiding in the joining of the solder to the electrodes, a good flux will prevent bridging of nonmetallized margins by the solder. Obviously the residual flux must be noncorrosive and, for electronic devices, nonconductive. Such characteristics are not at once evident.

Solutions of pine rosin in various solvents have a time honored record of safety. Some of the so-called "activated rosin" fluxes may be just as safe, but many have also been responsible for defective connections. It is not the purpose here to enter the debate as to which are safe and which are not. Literature on the subject is incomplete, conflicting and often expressed with words of vehemence. Remember this. If the electrodes do not solder well with plain rosin flux, something may be wrong with either the materials or the methods of applying the electrodes.

Let us, for the moment, assume that we *do* have in our possession a perfectly safe activated rosin flux, that is, one that leaves no corrosive or electrically conductive residues. Soldering *per se* is not our goal. We want to solder only those electrodes that are up to accepted standards, not the good and the bad alike.

Here is an actual case history that will illustrate the point in mind. A rush order of capacitors for an important customer fared very poorly when the units got to final inspection. A systematic check was started down the line. One cause of rejections for low "Q" was found to be due to the use of a hitherto untried activated flux, a material "guaranteed to end your soldering woes." No doubt about it—the connections involved were *really soldered!*

An immediate change was made back to the regular flux which was a proprietary rosin alcohol solution. Now there was failure of another sort. The electrodes soldered poorly, with indications of scavenging, or else not at all. Here was the reason why the sample of activated flux had been pulled off the shelf.

Watch Electroding Procedures

Continuing down the line, the electroding procedures were found to be the cause of the poor solderability and some of the electrical failures. As often happens in such instances, the trouble was not due to one but a combination of abuses. For one thing, the silver paint had been thinned with too much solvent, and this naturally led to thin electrodes. In addition, the paint was being underfired, which caused poor adherence and scavenging in the solder pot.

Now, the point to be made is this. Not all silver paints, on all ceramic bodies, can be soldered with equal facility. When difficulties are encountered, one should be certain that preceding operations have been performed correctly before trying something else. And if that something else should be an activated flux, by all means test it thoroughly before throwing it on the line.

Another one of the problems associated with soldering is that of thermal shock to the ceramic body. A good start in the right direction can be made by taking care that the ceramic has not already been shocked during previous operations. For example, nonuniform or rapid cooling during the body or silver firing stages often induces incipient strains. Then the soldering operation gets blamed for subsequent failures when, actually, it only administered the *coup d'ètat*.

How To Avoid Thermal Shock

But, assuming that we have a pretty good ceramic up to this point, the sudden immersion in a pot of solder at about 425° F. is still fairly rough treatment. With thin components and some bodies no trouble is experienced. Others just can't take it. The two methods about to be described have proven very successful in circumventing thermal shock with sensitive bodies. Both have one feature in common—they provide an intermediate preheating step before immersion in the solder pot.

The components may be coated with flux, the solvents driven off, and then preheated in a wax bath (such as Glyco S-932) operated at a temperature of 225° F. Keep the ceramic in the bath for a few seconds, say five, giving thick sections a proportionally longer time.

The second method is probably the best of all because it calls for preheating in essentially a high temperature flux. This bath is formulated by dissolving 350 grams of rosin (Hercules "commercial abietic acid") in 650 cc. of butyl lactate over a water bath. When the resin is dissolved, add another 650 cc. of butyl lactate. This is the stock solution and may be further thinned with the solvent to adjust the working viscosity.

The pot of flux is maintained at about 225° F. The ceramic components are dipped into the heated flux for a few seconds, until they come up to the flux temperature, then dipped immediately into the molten solder. Result: Well-fluxed silver surfaces, a minimum of thermal shock, good solder wetting and joints of optimum strength.

Do Not Operate Too Hot

Avoid the mistake of operating the pot at too high a temperature. The thermal capacity of the solder pot, hence the size, must be in line with the size of the articles being soldered. Use the lowest operating temperature commensurate with good soldering, and provide thermostatic conrtol of the heating elements. Higher temperatures than needed increase the chances for heat-shocking the ceramic, cause excessive dross to form, inhibit the desirable action of the flux and increase the cooling temperature differential.

Hardwood, spring clothespins or stainless steel tweezers, either "as is" or suitably modified, will hold parts for soldering on a small run basis. Production fixtures of stainless steel can be designed for specific jobs. Aluminum has been used for this purpose, but contamination of the solder by even a small amount of this metal degrades the wetting action.

Custom fixtures are expensive. Anyone can sit down and "design" one in a few minutes—you know the type—springs here, clamps there, a unit of cost of $25 and the promise of a 3-month delivery! And that is only the initial cost of an unduly complicated fixture. There are maintenance costs to be considered, and they must be cleaned frequently.

You are well advised to "look before you leap"—even if it's in m'lady's handbag! You think that's far fetched? Hundreds of thousands of small ceramic electronic assemblies have been held for soldering on a conveyor line with, of all things, bobby pins. The fixture cost? Less than one cent each!

Soldering with Iron

Dip soldering is not applicable to all production jobs, although it is certainly the method easiest adapted to automation. It is much more difficult to control the amount of heat applied to the work when a copper bit "iron" is used.

It seems obvious that the size of the iron should be dictated by the job at hand, yet the author once saw 150-watt irons in use on small ceramic printed circuits .020 inches thick. Rejections because of cracking amounted to 50% but were dismissed as being due to "poor ceramics"! It was the first production order, and they admitted to "having a *little* trouble getting started."

A switch to pencil soldering irons with 23½-watt tips (such as the Ungar units) reduced cracked assemblies to a negligible amount.

Once a certain electric soldering iron has been selected for the job (leave irons heated with blow-torches to the plumbers!), the temperature of the tip may be controlled, within limits, by the distance it projects from the heating head bore.

If there is any doubt about whether the ceramic will take the thermal shock, here is a little trick that helps. Wave the end of the iron slowly over the piece, gradually bringing it up to temperature. In a couple of minutes you can apply the solder. This saves the time it would take to preheat the components in an oven.

Copper Tip Should Be Cleaned

It hardly seems necessary to advise that the copper tip should be cleaned with a file at regular intervals and returned to its original form. When it comes to tips, don't think you have a choice of a pyramid or chisel shape, and that's that. For the 100-watt-plus irons, there is a little melting pot available that holds about an ounce of solder. It is one inch in diameter, one inch deep, costs about $1.00 and will probably pay for itself on the first job.

Some bodies with fired-on silver electrodes or patterns are particularly difficult to solder in spite of good electroding and soldering practices. Such bodies call for special materials and pretreatments before they can be soldered. Anything that makes for a fast operation reduces the scavenging, and burnishing the silver is often all that is required.

In the laboratory, a few strokes with a pencil eraser will provide enough burnishing action. For those who find that tedious, even this simple operation can be mechanized by making use of an electric erasing machine of the kind manufactured for draftsmen's use. Actually, quite a number of ways could be devised for burnishing on a unit basis. The real question is, how can this be done economically to a considerable quantity of small components?

How About Ball Milling?

A rather obvious method that at once suggests itself is to roll the parts in a ball mill. All well and good, except for one thing. The tumbling and rolling action of ball-milling tends to smear silver across insulating margins. The result—shorts. There is an answer, however, and it provides a very satisfactory solution. Try this one "for size" and you may throw away those super charged solder fluxes you have been using for the tough ones.

Take a wide-mouth, quart glass bottle and load it with the components until it is nearly full. Then fill the jar with 190-proof, denatured ethyl alcohol. Clamp the jar in a vibratory paint mixer and shake for several minutes. The time will have to be determined by trial. It varies with the body, size of the components and extent of electroding, but will be in the order of 3 to 30 minutes. This kind of burnishing action does not smear electrodes, nor does it cause chipped edges due to tumbling.

Use Fresh Alcohol for Each Batch

A word of warning—don't forget to fill the jar with components or they will have room enough to move about. And, use fresh alcohol for each batch—it doesn't cost *that* much!

Ideally, for a specific set-up, ceramic capacitors for example, a vibratory shaker can be designed just for the job. Frequently and amplitude could be independently variable. In the simplest case, the frequency would be a multiple of 60 cycles and the amplitude adjusted by limit stops.

Failing to get adequate soldering action by practicing the preceding arts, all is not lost. We can find more ways to solder than they can to skin cats! Excellent solderability of the fired-on type of electrodes can be obtained by electroplating. Often a thin copper plate will do the job. Or the electrodes can be plated with copper, then with silver, and then soldered. For the *pièce de résistance* you can match the composition of the solder itself. Yes, even a 60:40 tin-lead plated deposit is possible.

Of course, when electroplating is to be done, special silver paints must be used for the electrodes. These call for certain firing precautions and associated techniques. Some unique problems arise in the plating process, too, which can be attributed to the specific gravity of the ceramic, the fact that only parts of it have been made electrically conductive, etc.

Some changes are usually necessary in commercial plating equipment. Regardless, electroplating is not as difficult as it may seem, but the procedures, control of solutions, etc., are too detailed for further discussion here.

Fluxless Soldering

So-called "fluxless soldering" produces cavitation in the solder with ultrasonic energy literally to blast oxide films away from the basis metal. Most of the current designs of ultrasonic solder pots and irons are built around magnetostriction devices, although there is at least one model where the *tour de force* is provided by a ceramic piezoelectric transducer. The technique has received the most publicity because of the comparative ease with which such materials as aluminum, magnesium, germanium and silicon can be soldered. However, even with metals like copper and silver, ones that solder easily, doing away with the flux is advantageous.

CHAPTER XXIII

CONDUCTIVE COATINGS FOR CERAMICS

C. ALAN LINDQUIST, JR.

Astatic Corp.

The developments that have taken place in ceramic technology in the past few years are wonderful to contemplate. Not only do we have new ceramic materials and techniques, but new applications for the old ceramics. Though no one can deny the material advances in the ceramic sciences, it is interesting to conjecture as to how much of the newness is merely a change in attitude. Ceramics *per se* are as "old as the hills." Indeed, their raw materials *are* the hills.

It is a real source of pleasure to observe the frequency with which other engineering disciplines are rediscovering "ceramics" as they optimize their designs. Name the field—atomic energy, missile research, machine tool manufacture, electronics—the best and most recent expressions include ceramic products. The satellites now circling the earth contain ceramic components.

Need for Conductive Coatings

Many of these new ceramic products require electrically conductive coatings for electrodes, shielding or wiring. It is about some of these materials that these chapters will be concerned, in particular, those used in the manufacture of printed circuitry, capacitors and transducers. For quantities produced and in dollar volume such applications are probably by far the largest consumers of conductive coating materials.

The best capacitor or transducer bodies are of little use without electrodes. Conductors are the very *modus operandi* of printed circuits. Unfortunately the selection of appropriate materials and techniques appears deceptively simple. Take any proprietary silver paint, follow the broad recommendations of the manufacturer for application and firing, and you have electrodes. However, it is also pretty sure that you have somewhat less than the best. The cost and quality of the final product may be largely determined by practices followed right at this stage.

About Solderability

For example, let's isolate one property—solderability—since this is so important in the manufacture of electronic components. To begin with, under-, or overfired silver paints may not solder at all! Or, it may take so long for the solder to wet the electrode that the ceramic body may be subjected to excessive thermal shock. If that happens, the piece may show discernable breaks right at the soldering station, or, worse yet, the defect may not show up until the final test, several operations later. Underfired electrodes, or selection of the wrong composition, will result in scavenging of the silver in the solder pot. This will give less conductive area than anticipated.

Defective components waste materials. That is particularly amoral to most engineers. Today, however, engineers and managers alike are deeply concerned with labor costs. Aside from labor lost in rejects, imperfect electrodes may double or even triple the soldering time. Automated production lines require even greater control. Solderability is, of course, only one of the many properties that may be affected by electroding techniques.

Generally speaking, proprietary coating materials are purchased for the production of electronic components. The manufacture of these paints has become a highly specialized business, time indurated, and fraught with secretive procedures. Only a few corporations compete in this field, and the formulations they offer are certainly not innumerable. What does this mean to the consumer? Make your own? Few have the particular know-how requisite for this. Then, too, it is usually best to leave such manufacture up to the specialists.

Does this mean that we need know nothing about the compositions? Definitely not. In fact, they can be altered to improve certain properties. And let's remember that the supplier of the paint may be the expert at formulation but *you* can—indeed, should—become the expert at application.

Air-Drying Silver Paints

Ceramic applications for these paints are somewhat limited. They depend upon polished silver flake for their electrical conductivity and organic plastics, such as butyl methacrylate, for the permanent binder. The viscosity is adjusted with solvents—butyl alcohol, butyl acetate, butyl "Cellosolve," toluol—depending upon the drying time desired. Some compositions contain a plastic binder that is thermosetting in character and, thus, require oven baking. However, the electrical conductivity of any of these paints (on the order of 2 ohms per square *), as well as the scratch resistance, can be improved by baking. These preparations find greatest application for shielding purposes on organic based materials.

Air-drying silver paints may aid preliminary design work. For example, capacitor or printed circuit designs can be "guesstimated" by paint-samples with these paints. The capacities will not be as great as equal areas of the fired-on silvers, but a correlative factor can be applied. Usually the

---

* The conductivity of paints is usually given in "ohms per square." The assumption is that the thickness dimension is not significant and that a square area of any size—$\frac{1}{8}$, $\frac{1}{4}$, 2 inches on a side—would always have the same resistance for any one material. This is essentially correct, and makes a most convenient way of placing the conductivity on a unit basis. To determine the resistance of a conductor, from end to end, use the width as unity and determine the number of such "squares" along the length. If, say, the line is 20 times as long as it is wide, and the resistance of the paint is 2 ohms per square, then the conductor is 40 ohms in resistance.

ratio of several capacitances to one another is all that is necessary, in any event.

An application, not so well known, where an air-drying material actually supplies the *tour de force* is the case of temporary electrodes for electro-mechanical transducers. To illustrate, a torsionally responsive device can be fabricated from a ferroelectric ceramic, such as barium titanate, by poling the material in certain directions and then using somewhat oppositely arranged electrodes for operation. The air-drying silver supplies the temporary electrodes for poling, after which they are eliminated with solvents. The operating electrodes may be of the fired-on type, in which case they must have been applied prior to poling, or of the air-dried type and, consequently, definitely limited to certain ambient conditions.

Do Not Overlook Carbon Electrodes

At first glance the use of carbon, in its various forms, for conductive electrodes does not seem wise, for we usually think of carbon in terms of its relatively high resistivity. Of course, carbon films can be laid down that will have a resistance of only a few hundred ohms per square. This is a low resistance for carbon but high compared with silver. Additionally, it is obvious that the use of carbon precludes direct soldering. Despite these objections, carbon electrodes definitely have some very important ceramic applications.

Carbon—in the form of lampblack, furnace black, channel black, acetylene black or graphite—is the basis for printed electronic circuit resistors. It is dispersed in a resinous system (an urea-formaldehyde modified epoxy, for example) with the working and drying properties adjusted with various solvents. The resistors are silk-screened onto ceramic base plates and cured *in situ*.

If the base plate has a low dielectric constant, there is little more than the resistance to consider. But, on the other hand, if the base plate has a high dielectric constant, then some secondary effects arise. The resistor itself may act as one electrode of a capacitor especially if it is opposed on the other side of the dielectric by another conductive material. This may alter markedly the desired electrical characteristics of the circuit. Even on the same side of the base plate the interaction of resistors with other conductors may give rise to untoward distributed capacitance. The designer of printed circuitry must weigh such effects carefully.

Use Capacitive Effects of Resistors

Somewhat akin to the, "If you can't fight them, join them" idea, these capacitive effects of printed resistors can be purposefully engineered into a circuit. Without going further into the design of printed circuits, suffice it to say that the series resistance-capacitance effects of high resistance electrodes are used in so-called "lumped parameter" circuits to eliminate discrete capacitors and resistors.

Dispersions of colloidal graphite are well known in the ceramic industry as high temperature lubricants (kiln cars, glass molds, etc.) Of the many dispersions available perhaps the best known is *Aquadag* ("aqua" for the menstruum, water, and "dag" for dispersed Acheson graphite). However, *Aquadag* is just one of many dispersions available. Mediums other than water are often desirable if not mandatory.

It is not at all surprising that this versatile material should turn up in the electronic industry with many uses around ceramic components. For example, in vacuum tubes, coatings of colloidal graphite absorb light, reduce undesired thermionic emissions, act as "getters" and make effective anodes. Applied externally, such films act as electrostatic shields for radio tubes and other components.

The audio industry is producing ceramic electro-mechanical transducers in ever increasing numbers. For reasons which must be sidestepped in this article, these transducers are fabricated as sandwich-type structures. Alternating through their thickness are three electrodes and two ceramic slabs. This construction makes what is called a "bender."

Squeegees covered with conductive silver paint are used to force paint through a fine mesh screen to form an electrical circuit on cerami plates. Painted components are known as "packaged electronic circuits."

Outer and Inner Electrodes

Now, the two outer electrodes are best made of a fired-on type of silver which is lasting and can be soft-soldered if necessary. The inner electrode, however, functions only during the poling of the ceramic slabs, the process by which they take on piezoelectric properties. There is no reason why this central electrode can't be made of a fired silver too, but, for certain transducer designs, it is much simpler to suck a graphite dispersion through suitable holes in the ceramic.

The low viscosity of the dispersion insures good coverage of the internal surfaces, and, when dried, this coating is quite adequate for purposes of polarizing the ceramic. The series resistance of the graphite film only serves to increase the time constant by an amount which has no significance here.

Here we have the ultimate in stability, conductivity, and physical properties for the silver paint compositions. These paints use ceramic materials in their formulations and ceramic techniques in application. Hence we can expect the durability associated with ceramics. The resistance is about 0.01 ohms per square, the lowest of the materials discussed thus far.

Many paints can be formulated or purchased. Some of these are essentially the same as the "liquid brights" used for decorating. Others are

Conductive coatings used to build a circuit on a ceramic base plate. Printed connections are of silver. Component leads are spot-welded to the platinum supports.

fairly low viscosity suspensions of precious metals such as platinum, palladium, gold and silver. Most of these materials have found use in electronics.

As mentioned previously, it is the intent of these articles to concentrate on those conductive paints that find greatest application to the manufacture of ceramic electronic components. In general, paints for these applications are of a much higher viscosity than the liquid metal suspensions and the liquid brights. The term "paint" will be used here because it has the advantage of the widespread usage. Actually, "paste" would be much more descriptive. Anyhow, these compositions contain a noble metal, usually silver, a ceramic binder, called a "flux," a temporary organic binder and solvents to regulate such important characteristics as viscosity and drying time.

Silver As A Conductor

The value of silver metal as an electrical conductor is well known, but other metals, such as copper, are good conductors too. Why, then, is silver the preferred metal for these paints? Some authors have chosen to justify the use of silver on the basis that its "corrosion products are conductive" or that it is "one of the few metals that has the faculty of being highly conductive in several of its forms, including oxide or sulfide." This is not entirely correct!

Reference to a basic text on the subject of silver discloses that there is little tendency of silver to form many "corrosion products" under normal conditions. It does tarnish fairly rapidly, much to the dismay of housewives, because of the action of atmospheric sulfides. The silver sulfide formed, however, has a protective action against further tarnishing. It is also true that, for a compound, silver sulfide has a fairly high electrical conductivity as compared with the corrosion products of other metals.[1]

What appears most interesting is what Zickrick[2] has to say about the electrical conductivity of silver oxide:

"All metal oxides are of high electrical resistivity; in fact, most may be classified as insulators. It has frequently been reported and published in the literature that silver is a good contact material because its oxide is a good conductor. This is not true. Silver oxide has a very high resistance, as has been found from measurements taken on carefully prepared samples. Values ranging from 40 to 50 megohms/cm.[3] have been obtained on pure silver oxide."

"Silver oxide, however, is one of the unstable oxides at elevated temperature, and when heated to 300–350° C. it readily decomposes, giving up its oxygen, and becoming pure silver. It is doubtless this property which has been responsible for such erroneous belief. . . . "

Again, why silver? Well, it has a high electrical conductivity. And, we learn that it really is a "noble metal"—under normal atmospheric conditions it does not form a *host* of corrosion products. The one formed is silver sulfide which, though far from being the conductor like silver, really isn't too bad for a compound. Even this corrosion product exhibits a protective action. Finally, silver oxide, a material of high resistivity, does not form in significant quantities.

Are Silver Paints Expensive?

Mention of silver naturally poses the question of expense. Happily, its noble qualities notwithstanding, these paints are not particularly expensive. To illustrate, a prepared paint costing $1.20 per ounce will cover about four square feet. That makes the cost per unit component rather low. On the other hand, these are not materials for painting the factory walls and floors. Good housekeeping is indicated.

The preferred metal for most paints is a leaf or flake silver produced mechanically from a very fine, chemically reduced precipitate. A thin coating of stearic acid makes the flake easy to disperse in organic vehicles. Fifty to 70% of the total weight of the conductive paint will be silver metal. Most of this is flake silver, although up to 10%, may be unpolished precipitated silver. In addition to both of these, silver oxide can be added for certain purposes. This will be discussed later.

The Metallic Resinates

For sake of completeness, the metallic resinates should be mentioned. These can be applied to the thick paste-type electroding materials as well as the low viscosity solutions. Resinates are obtained by a number of reactions. Silver oxide, silver carbonate or silver acetate can be reacted with one of the *Glyptals* (General Electric), *Ester Gum* (Hercules' glycerol ester of rosin) or *Rosin Amine D* (Hercules' technical grade of dehydroabietylamine). The charge is placed in a *Pyrex* flask equipped with some means for agitation. Reaction is carried out over a water bath with provision made for cooling to keep the exothermic reaction within bounds.

CHAPTER XXIV

HOW TO APPLY CONDUCTIVE COATINGS

C. Alan Lindquist, Jr.
Astatic Corp.

Some means must be provided for bonding the metal to the body. Any number of simple glasses would do the job, but the problem is not solved as easily as that. For any one body, the amount and kind of flux will determine adherence, solderability, chemical durability, electrical conductivity, maturing temperature, etc. Some compromises have to be made, and, as we might suspect, no one flux will serve as an electroding panacea.

Three Groups of Fluxes

Fluxes can be broadly classified into three groups—bismuth oxide, lead borate and lead borosilicate. These can be used alone or in combination with each other to tailor-make fluxes for various applications. Silver bonded with calcined bismuth oxide has excellent direct soldering qualities and high electrical conductivity. Adherence, however, is not as good as can be obtained with the others. Capacitor electrodes are frequently bonded with 5 to 11% of bismuth oxide.

Paints intended for mica will have about 5% of a lead borate and sometimes a lead borosilicate. Excellent adherence to many ceramic bodies is obtained with lead borosilicate fluxes. They also give the highest chemical durability which is especially important when electroplating must be performed. Quantities used range from 4 to 8%. Silver bonded with lead borosilicate is not suitable for direct soldering without special treatment, and the conductivity is lower.

Flux composition is just one parameter to consider. For example, a high ratio of silver to flux will give greater electrical conductivity, better solderability, but lower adherence. And what is the intended function of the component—capacitor, transducer? Flux ratios and compositions must be juggled to optimize for each set of conditions.

Good Application Essential

Visual examination of fired silver electrodes may disclose the way in which the paint was applied, but one can only guess at the organic materials that made successful coating possible. The best possible combination of inorganic materials is of no avail if the application has been poor. Once the paint has been applied in a uniform film, it must have the correct drying properties. When dried, it must have adequate strength to prevent dusting without being brittle. Finally, during the firing process the organic binder must burn completely without carbonization and without disruption of the paint.

129

Time was when beeswax, mutton tallow, rosin, balsam fir oil, French fat oil, stearates and many other natural products constituted the soul and substance of application media. We must not be deprecatory toward these natural products for, despite the vagaries of their compositions, when correctly blended they are hard to beat. Regardless, today most of us will find it much easier to start with some of the synthesized raw materials.

Ethyl Cellulose Binder

One of the most widely used binders in silver paste preparations is ethyl cellulose, a cellulose ether resulting from the reaction of ethyl chloride and alkali cellulose. Look at the advantages. It has great flexibility over a wide range of temperatures. It dissolves in many solvents making possible a variety of application methods. It is tough and stable. It burns gently without leaving carbonaceous residues.

Four types of ethyl cellulose are available from the Hercules Powder Co. Of these the "N-Type" (ethoxyl content of 47.5 to 49%) is the most common. It can be purchased in seven viscosity ranges—7, 10, 14, 22, 50, 100 and 200 cps. The 50 and 200 cps. types seem to work out quite well in a variety of silver paints. About 2 to 5% by weight will be used.

TABLE I
Properties of solvents

Solvent	Specific Gravity 20/20° C.	Boiling Point ° F.	Vapor Pressure mm. Hg @ 20° C.
Methanol	0.7924	148	96.1
Ethyl Acetate	0.9018	171	74.4
Water	1.0000	212	17.5
Toluol	0.867	230	......
n-Butyl Alcohol	0.8109	241	5.5
Butyl Acetate	0.8826	260	7.8
"Cellosolve"	0.9311	275	3.7
Xylene	0.865	277	10.05
Amyl Alcohol	0.815	280	2.9
Gum Turpentine	0.867	311	......
"Cellosolve" Acetate	0.9748	313	1.2
Butyl "Cellosolve"	0.9019	340	0.7
n-Butyl Lactate	0.980	383	0.4
Pine Oil	0.9426	399	......
"Carbitol" Acetate	1.0114	423	0.05
Butyl "Carbitol"	0.9536	447	0.02
Butyl "Carbitol" Acetate	0.9810	457	<0.01
Glycerin	1.2609	554	(decomposes)

There is limited application for an aqueous medium, and again the cellulose family provides the answer. Methyl cellulose, that valuable binder for drypress mixes and glazes, makes a good binder for these conductive paints. Dow *Methocel* (dimethyl ether of cellulose) is available in nine viscosity types—10, 15, 25, 50, 100, 400, 1500, 4000 and 7000 cps.

Factors in Paint Viscosity

The viscosity of the paint will depend upon (1) the inorganic material particle size, (2) the type of organic binder selected, and (3) the proportion of inorganic solids, organic solids, solvents, diluents, plasticizers and stabilizers (if any).

The state of subdivision of the silver and the frit will be fixed by considerations other than viscosity relationships. In one respect the amount of rosin should be sufficient to give the desired film strength and no more. But then there is the matter of viscosity. Within limits, equiviscous solutions of high viscosity or large amounts of low viscosity resins. It is all a matter of judicious compromise. Whatever solvents are introduced have to be removed during the drying stage, and the more used, the greater the drying shrinkage. Similarly, the rosin added burns out during firing and contributes toward shrinkage.

These considerations are of more than casual interest because they can affect the electrical properties of the fired silver. Excessive shrinkage may cause the conductive particles to separate enough to lower the conductivity and the Q factor.

Viscosity and Drying Speed

Carrying on with the same thought, we remember that a large part of the metal content is likely to be flake silver. The viscosity and speed of drying of the vehicle is going to determine to some extent how much alignment there will be with these platy particles.

The solvent system selected must, first of all, depend upon the rosin, or rosins, which go to make up the binder. It is seldom desirable to use a

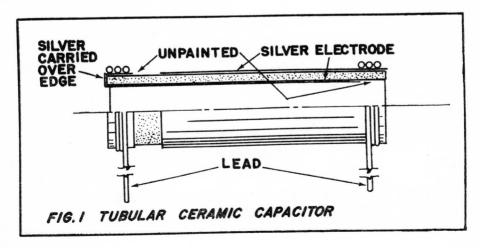

FIG. 1 TUBULAR CERAMIC CAPACITOR

1-component system. A blend of two or more solvents will result in good solubility over a wider range of conditions. A combination of the right solvents can also result in a marked lowering of viscosity.

The evaporation rate will naturally depend upon the solvents selected, and, with two or more components, it can be made to proceed gradually over a wide range of temperatures up to and including the decomposition point of the rosin itself. Thus the paints can be made to dry quickly, under normal ambient conditions, or can be made to remain essentially unchanged for months under the same conditions.

Method Determines Drying

The application method will determine how fast the paint should dry. It is a relative thing, of course, for a silk screen paint can be brushed, and a brushing paint can be screened. Usually, though, the dipping paints will have the lowest boiling solvents as well as the lowest viscosities. Spraying paints come next. Brush or roller coating materials require sufficient drying time for adequate flowout of the brush or wheel marks.

The squeegee or screening paints will be more paste-like and contain the "high boilers." The essentials for a good silk screen paint are that it be viscous enough not to run, yet thin enough to go through the screen without clogging. It must have "body" and, since relatively large amounts are spread out on the screen at one time, must not dry significantly at room temperature. Brushing, of course, is different. The area exposed is not as great and, what with vertical surfaces involved, some ambient drying is innately desirable.

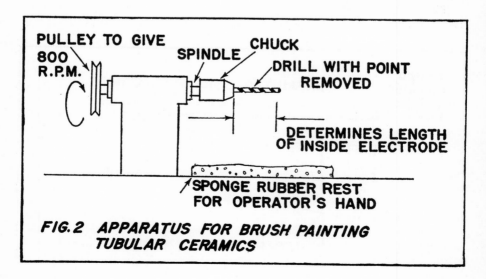

PULLEY TO GIVE 800 R.P.M.
SPINDLE
CHUCK
DRILL WITH POINT REMOVED
DETERMINES LENGTH OF INSIDE ELECTRODE
SPONGE RUBBER REST FOR OPERATOR'S HAND

FIG. 2 APPARATUS FOR BRUSH PAINTING TUBULAR CERAMICS

Experimentation with Solvent System

Some experimentation is necessary to set up the solvent system that will give the desired viscosity and drying properties. Individual preferences play an important part. Toluol, butyl acetate and butyl lactate can be blended to give dipping paints. Brushing and banding formulations may contain toluol, butyl lactate, butyl "Carbitol" or pine oil. Squeegee paints will contain combinations of butyl "Cellosolve," butyl lactate, "Carbitol" acetate, butyl "Carbitol" and butyl "Carbitol" acetate. A list of representative solvents and some of their properties is given in Table I.

The introduction to the "materials" section of this article made clear that the manufacture of conductive paints is highly specialized business. With few exceptions, silver paint will be purchased as a raw material formulated for the intended application. Nonetheless, it cannot be taken off the storage shelf and placed into direct use on the production line without at least a little preparation. If nothing else, the contents of the jar should be mixed thoroughly to insure homogeneity. This can be accomplished easily by 20 minutes' shaking on a mixer such as the Arlington midget paint restorer.

Viscosity Too High

Experience may show that the viscosity in the "as received" condition is too high and that some solvent should be added. Viscosity determinations can be made with a Brookfield viscometer or a No. 4 Ford type viscosity cup ($\frac{1}{8}''$ opening). The Ford cup method involves measuring the time in seconds for a fixed volume of the paint to flow through the orifice.

The cup can be surrounded with a constant temperature bath, but factory practice does not usually require this refinement if a temperature of $75° \pm 5°$ F. is specified for the measurement. When the same thinner, or thinners, is used every time, the consistency can be tied down by a weight specification. The following is an example—175 ± 5 grams per 100 ml.

It would seem safe to say that in not too many cases will the choice of a production application method be very difficult. Naturally you are not going to consider screening as a possible way for coating the inside surfaces of a tube, or a transfer wheel as a means of forming the complicated outlines of printed circuits. But, getting away from these obvious absurdities, the decision is often not clear cut. The situation is this: some organizations develop an application method to the very pinnacle of refinement by the acquisition of unique know-how or by equipment capitalization. They will then favor this one method.

The shape of the object to receive the electrodes, its physical condition, the thickness of coating desired—all determine to some extent the application means. Small tubular components can be dipped or brushed. Or perhaps the paint will be rolled on with a transfer wheel. Flat surfaces can be sprayed, screened, dipped or brushed. Holes in the body may have to be coated by dragging the paint through on some carrier. Aspiration sometimes provides a simple expediency. But these are mechanical ways. Chemical deposition must not be forgotten—it has been widely practiced.

Brushing Is Likely Method

Regardless of the condition of the surface or the shape of the component, brushing is nearly always a possibility. The chances are good that the laboratory or engineering samples were prepared this way, but the method has production possibilities too—up to a certain point. The tooling costs are low. A production line can be set up quickly. Changes can often be effected in minutes. And let's not forget one salient feature—there's nothing like a brush for working paint onto a surface. Sure there is the possibility of brush marks, but for a really good job you can double the coat.

If the component includes surfaces of revolution, brushing may be very easy. Take a hemispherical object for example. Suppose that the convex and concave surfaces must be covered, leaving a margin at the edge. A simple jig can be made to match one surface for holding, allowing the other surface to be exposed for painting. The jig can be arranged on a vertically aligned spindle and then rotated. It is a simple matter to pick up some paint on a brush and, with an upward motion, coat the exposed surface uniformly.

Many Components Tube-Shaped

Many electronic components, notably ceramic capacitors, are in the shape of tubes. A cross-section of one type of capacitor is shown in Fig. 1. In essence it consists of two electrodes—one inside and one outside. Since it is not convenient to connect a lead to the inner electrode on the tube i.d., this electrode is painted over the end of the tube and carried a small distance, say .070″, over the tube o.d. This enables an electrical connection to be made to this electrode by means of a lead wrapped around the outside of the tube.

Suitable margins, usually no less than .060″, are provided between the two electrodes, inside and out. Since the capacitance must be reckoned only on the basis of the portions of the two plates that *oppose* each other (except for " fringe capacity"), somewhat less than optimum utilization of the dielectric medium results. This is not serious. Every American manufacturer places both leads on the outside.

Electrodes Brush On Easily

Electrodes are brushed on easily with rather simple equipment. All that is required is a rotating spindle terminated by a drill chuck as illustrated in Fig. 2. The spindle is made to rotate slowly enough to keep the peripheral speed of the tube below that which would throw off the paint. About 800 r.p.m. will satisfy these conditions. Depending upon the size of the tube, either a twist drill (with the point ground away) or a piece of a pipe cleaner is inserted into the chuck. Pipe cleaners can be doubled back on themselves to give twice the diameter. Drills, on the other hand, come in a variety of sizes, so that it is easy to select one that will rotate easily in any particular tube. There must be enough clearance in order to allow for warpage.

The distance that the drill or pipe cleaner projects from the chuck determines the length of the inside electrode. The part that shorts over the end is obtained by brushing paint against the end of the drill chuck. Paint on the outside of the tube is applied with a brush.

How to Gauge These Areas

The question arises as how to gauge these areas. This is done by means of pointed wires held in a fixture as shown in Fig. 3. However, the points are not observed directly. It will be understood that if the points were far enough from the tube so as not to interfere with the painting operation, there would be sufficient space to give parallax. This problem is circumvented by placing a light bulb in a reflector, in back of the gauge wires and arranged so that the light is shielded from the operator's eyes but such that shadows of the points are cast on the rotating tube. The operator must paint up to the shadow edge, not into the shadow. It is easy to see that if one painted into the shadow the margin would be very difficult to estimate.

The painting sequence may be varied somewhat. However, the following description will be illustrative of the complete operation. The operator set the gauge points by means of a "standard," slips a tube over the spindle, loads the brush with paint, then proceeds to paint the out-

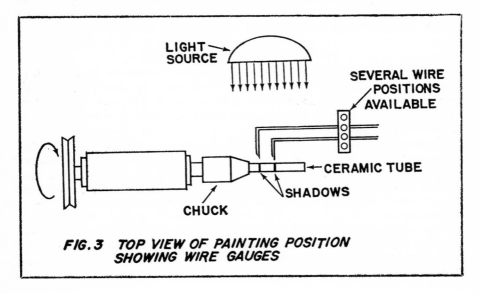

FIG. 3 TOP VIEW OF PAINTING POSITION SHOWING WIRE GAUGES

side areas of the tube. The tube is then removed from the spindle with tweezers machined to fit the i.d. Painted tubes are placed vertically on peg boards and passed through the drying oven. After this they are placed in trays and put through the firing kiln.

Inside Electrode Painted

Now, the inside or "hot" electrode is painted. A suitable drill is placed in the chuck and adjusted to project a distance that will give the desired capacity. Then the operator brushes paint against the end of the chuck and along the drill. A tube, correctly oriented with regard to the fired electrode, is placed on the drill and pushed up against the end of the chuck with a twisting motion counter to that of the spindle rotation. The tube is then removed and placed in a tray for drying and firing.

The process just described for painting the "hot" electrodes can be adapted to semiautomatic operation. Fixtures are made to hold a number of tubes in a vertical position. These pass to a paint station where they are located on a jig over a pan of silver paint. Located in the paint are several drills, aligned vertically with the same horizontal spacing as the tubes in the fixture, and connected at their bases by small gears to affect rotation. The pan of paint is lowered away from the drills and the drills raised to enter the ceramic tubes. Loading and unloading of the tube holding fixtures is semiautomatic.

Disk capacitors can also be painted by brushing methods. For example, the disks can be automatically loaded into depressions in a moving belt and forwarded to a brush position. At this station the disks can be held by vacuum applied to the underside and a measured drop of paint allowed to fall on the upper surface. Then a rotating, somewhat stiff, brush can be lowered to wipe the paint around the surface.

Must Have Sharply Defined Margins

Ceramic capacitors must have sharply defined margins. This is necessary for two reasons: (1) The capacity is controlled by the location of the margins, and (2) an insulating barrier is needed to withstand high potentials (1500 vdc). For these reasons the dipping of paint on capacitors has not been too successful.

Various methods have been devised for "dipping to capacity." The inner electrode of a tube can be applied in some way, a sealing compound placed on the lower end to prevent paint from entering, and then the tube lowered slowly into a bowl of paint made conductive in the fluid state with an electrolyte. A capacity bridge would be connected to the inner electrode and the paint reservoir.

Transducers used in microphones and phonograph cartridges often take the form of small, elongated slabs which have been cut from larger sheets of matured ceramic. Each slab must be silvered completely on both sides. The silver can extend right up to the edge of the element.

Now, silvering each little piece of ceramic after cutting would be rather time consuming. Here is an application that is ideal for dipping. The large sheet is dipped into a tank of silver paint, drained, dried, and fired. The edges of the sheet are trimmed and then diced into the ultimate unit size.

Using Wheel Transfer

Most of us have heard of the banding operations performed on glassware. Thus it takes no great stretch of the imagination to visualize a method for electroding tubular ceramics in a somewhat similar fashion. Since these components are usually quite small—seldom larger than $\frac{1}{4}$ inch in diameter—they are best located by their i.d. Then the outside can be given an application of paint by rolling it on from wheels. The wheels may pick the paint up directly from a reservoir or else by transfer from another wheel which runs in a reservoir.

Two kinds of wheels can be considered. First is a wheel which is essentially the full width of the band to be painted on the ceramic. Or a thin wheel can be made to traverse the band width several times in one revolution of the ceramic tube. A simple way to do this is to spring load the wheel and have it bear against a cam. Both the wide and thin wheels work very effectively, but the thin wheel has, as one might expect, a better resolution.

We have all heard the spiritual which tells of "a wheel within a wheel." Well, the expression graphically describes an efficient painting set up. Ceramic tube holding pins are arranged on the periphery of a large wheel that rotates, in "lazy susan" fashion, to carry the tubes over a small paint transfer wheel. One station serves for load and unload, both of which can be automatic. During a portion of the revolution of the "lazy susan" the painted tubes pass through a small drying oven. This is a rather efficient method and one that can be changed rapidly to accommodate other sizes.

Object May Oscillate Instead of Wheel

In passing it might be mentioned that the object being painted can be made to oscillate instead of the paint wheel—the contact point can't tell which is doing the moving! However, since we are dealing with large numbers of small tubes, and a single paint wheel, it is quite evident that tooling, in this case, is much easier if the paint wheel does the traversing. No need to move the mountain when Mohammed can be prodded.

There is hardly any need to applaud the merits of spraying as a production tool for painting. Mica capacitors are made this way. A number of mica sheets are placed in a jig, a masking plate lowered over them and then the whole rack given a spray coating of silver.

When we come to small ceramic tubes, disks, and sheets, however, the picture is a little different. Their shapes, coupled with inherent warping, are against adequate delineation of margins by spray coating. Recovery of overspray is a factor too, especially when you are dealing with a material that costs between one and two dollars an ounce. Furthermore, sprayed electrodes are not as thick as those produced in other ways.

Screening for Large Scale Production

Screening is ideally suited for the large scale production of technical electronic ceramics. Of all the application processes described, screening is best for the reproduction of complex outlines. For this reason it is selected for most of the printed circuit work. Large numbers of ceramic capacitors are fabricated this way too.

Screens can be made of silk or stainless steel. Each plant seems to have its favorite way to mount the screens and present them to the ware. It is important to evaluate all screening materials—emulsions, masks, squeegees, etc.—in regard to their resistance to the paint solvents.

The process is inherently very flexible. Objects can be screened by an operator one at a time. One operator can also screen, with about the same effort, quite a number of pieces if means are provided for loading jigs. There again, the jigs can be loaded manually or automatically. In fact the whole thing can be mechanized.

The thickness of the film can be varied as desired, and yet, for any one set of conditions, the coating thickness will be uniformly deposited from one piece to another. The nature of the process demands a paint compounded with high boiling solvents so that its viscosity is stable under varying ambient conditions. This makes it possible to exercise better control over the drying process.

CHAPTER XXV

DRYING AND FIRING CONDUCTIVE COATINGS

C. Alan Lindquist, Jr.

Astatic Corp.

Once the paint has been applied to the surface, the organic components must be removed as gently as possible. Solvents must be driven off prior to firing or further handling. Some drying is bound to occur at room temperature, but this is seldom sufficient to eliminate additional drying at elevated temperatures. Improper drying can cause blistering and lifting of the coating. Establishment of correct drying practices may be old stuff in the ceramic industry, but electronic component manufacturers too often apply little more than slap-dab techniques!

Let's consider some illustrative examples. One plant dries silver by placing the racks on top of the kiln. The operators feel the surfaces to decide when the pieces are dry. When the rush is on, the ware gets a token drying step. In another plant the paint is dried under a crudely arranged bank of infrared lamps. The ware is placed on racks and manually pushed through the lamps.

Production Slow, Drying Complete

If production is slow, the drying is complete. When the paint lines are going full speed, the racks are shoved through as fast as necessary to keep the lines clear. An actual survey made in the four plants of one capacitor manufacturer disclosed that little regard was given to the particular kind of paint being dried, the temperature varied from 200° to 400° F. and the time from 3 to 30 minutes.

Sure you can get away with such practices. It is not a matter of "go" or "no go." The price paid is an over-all loading down of the operational efficiency. Some people think that all that is necessary to dry something is to slam it in an oven set for a certain temperature. All these problems can be bypassed by purchasing adequate equipment—continuous driers are best. The gradual rise in temperature creates the most desirable situation for solvent removal. It is not economical to attempt solvent recovery, but the vapors should be carried out of the plant.

Production Requirements Determine Firing Method

Production requirements will determine whether the firing should be done in a periodic or a tunnel kiln. An oxidizing atmosphere is mandatory and is simply obtained by exhausting the combustion products. The ware can be spread in a single layer on an asbestos coated stainless steel belt running through a continuous kiln. For batch kiln settings, or where mixed components are sent through one tunnel kiln, the ware should be placed in trays. These may be made of stainless steel, but some contamination is always present. The possible effect upon the completed product must be evaluated. One plant found that changing from stainless steel trays, a practice of 10 years, to claybonded stabilized zirconia, gave a substantial lowering of the power factor of ceramic capacitors.

Adherence, solderability and electrical properties are dependent upon proper firing cycles. Underfired electrodes appear dull and have little adherence to the ceramic. They will be subject to scavenging during the soldering operation. Overfired coatings will appear glazed. This glazed surface prevents soldering or electroplating.

Deliberate overfiring of silvers containing lead borosilicate fluxes, such as those intended for electroplating, has been turned to advantage. When these are matured at 1600° F. adherence to the ceramic body is really remarkable. The glazed surface, which would prohibit plating or soldering, is etched with fluoboric acid. Following etching, the ware is rinsed thoroughly, plated with acid copper, then plated with silver and finally passed to the soldering station. If you have an adherence problem, by all means try this.

Temperatures and Times

The manufacturer of the coating formulation will suggest recommended firing temperatures and times. However, the solution to proper firing rests in tests made with any particular furnace. Indicated temperature means little going from one kiln to another. Coating maturity is a heat-treatment, a product of time and temperature.

There are temperatures below and above which each silver paint must not be fired. Within these limits a drop or elevation of temperature necessitates a corresponding increase or decrease in the soaking time. The total cycle, from entrance to exit ends of the kiln, may be only 30 minutes. Schedules as short as this have to be very carefully planned in order to avoid heat shock after the ware passes the hot zone.

Once a certain cycle has been determined for a particular paint, in a particular kiln, the indicated temperature and the belt speed should maintain the correct heat-treatment *provided* that the thermal load is essentially constant. Remember, too, that with electrical furnaces the hot spot will migrate due to nonuniform wear of the resistance elements.

The foregoing has made clear that a firing schedule cannot be set down in black and white and expected to give optimum results everywhere.

How to Obtain Necessary Data

How does one go about obtaining necessary data? First of all, send samples of the painted components through the kiln under various time-temperature combinations. Next use solderability tests to provide clues to the electrode maturity. If the components are flat, cut a piece of rosin-core wire solder into equal lengths, form the pieces into tori, lay one of these on each test piece and send all of them through a soldering oven at one time. An examination of the way the solder wets the surface will point to the best firing cycle.

The same technique, only using samples fired at the recommended schedule and sent through the soldering oven under variable conditions, will enable one to evaluate the soldering operation itself.

Another Firing Check

Another way to check the firing is to dip the tubes or disks in rosin flux and then immerse them in a solder pot for 20 seconds. Remove, tap to fling off excess solder and permit to cool. Then soak in a solvent to remove excess flux, and examine surface conditions. Immature silver will dissolve in the solder leaving blackened areas. The longer the electrodes can remain in the solder without scavenging, the better. Overfired silver will not wet easily with solder. There should be no silvered areas showing through the solder. Severe cases of nonwetting will appear lace-like.

Finally, once these visual tests have pointed the way, electrical tests, where applicable, can narrow the firing limits still more. For example, ceramic capacitors, especially those where a close capacity tolerance must be maintained, can be heated in an oven to the solder pot temperature, removed, aged four hours and the capacity measured. Then they can be immersed in a pot of solder for, say, 15 seconds, again aged four hours and capacity measured. A reduction in capacitance may be attributed to electrode scavenging. The firing schedule which gives the least change in capacity is the one to follow.

Special Considerations

Just because proprietary paints are purchased is no reason to forget about formulating possibilities altogether. Every property of the paint can be modified to suit unique situations. Suppose, for example, that you have an application for a plating silver and, despite changes in the firing schedule, the surface becomes glazed. Try additions of 1 to 2% of Norton's 38900 alumina—the trouble will disappear.

When a paint has gelled, probably due to humid conditions, a few drops of a solution of soybean lecithin in pine oil and a little agitation will put it back in its original condition. In fact, any paint will be improved by the addition of this potent wetting agent. It "wets" better, so covers more surface.

The conductivity and solderability of a coating can be markedly improved by adding 30 to 40 grams of silver oxide to 100 grams of the paint. The organic binder, of course, must be increased along with the silver. This can be done by introducing 5 ml. of a 40% solution of Hercules *8L Imperial Ester Gum* in toluol. The added components must be thoroughly dispersed by ball milling for several hours.

A silk screen paint should be stiff enough so that it does not run through the screen. This very property somewhat limits the resolution that can be obtained because of cross-hatching by the screen. The ideal situation would be obtained if the paint would run just enough, after being laid down, to erase the mesh marks and yet not so much as to destroy the outline. As anyone who has played around considerably with these media knows, the end result is a compromise of all the desired characteristics.

A Useful Additive

Now, suppose that a substance could be added to the paint which would be very stiff at room temperatures and yet would change rapidly in viscosity as the temperature was raised during drying—enough to cause a slight flow of the paint? The problem would be solved. Well, there is just such a material—Hercules *Abitol* (technical hydroabietyl alcohol). The viscosity-temperature curve of *Abitol* is quite remarkable. From 40° to 100° C. the viscosity changes from 400 to 0.5 poises!

It is soluble in all the common organic solvents that might be contained in the silk screen media and is compatible in all proportions with ethyl cellulose. At room temperature the volatility is extremely low; at the silver paint drying temperatures it evaporates completely. What could be better? Up to 30% by volume can be added to paints for these improved screening properties. Warm both the paint and the *Abitol,* stir thoroughly with a low r.p.m., high torque mixer, and replace any solvents that are lost with butyl "Carbitol" acetate.

Effective Stop-Offs

The need for selective electroplating or etching does not arise often, but when it does a suitable resist or stopoff must be located. A material which will work very effectively for such purposes, although it is not marketed with this application in mind, is duPont's *RAC-906 Methacrylate Clear Finish.* Two thinners, duPont's T-3857 and T-3818, enable the air drying time, for a tack-free surface, to be varied from 10 minutes to 1 hour. The resin is supplied as a solution in a low boiling solvent. If this is removed and replaced with butyl "Carbitol" acetate, an effective screening medium will be obtained. The *RAC-906* resin is transparent but can be dyed or pigmented as is desired.

Certain tubular ceramic assemblies have metal ferrules soldered on the outside. Not infrequently the o.d. of the tube will have more than one electrode and, in assembling the ferrule—what with the close fit usually required—there is a good chance that silver will be smeared across the bare tube.

The possibility of electrical shorts from this source can be effectively prevented by a mechanical stop-off. Coat the tubes with a 25% solution of commercial abietic acid (Hercules rosin) in acetone, alcohol or toluol. When the rosin is dry, locate the metal rings and solder them in position. No additional fluxing is necessary—what could be better than the rosin itself?

Electroplating Often Desirable

There are many applications for electroplated ceramic components. This markedly improves solderability of conductors as there obtains a metal-to-metal wetting without interposed inorganic particles. Silver is the usual metal that is plated, although even a tin-lead composition can be deposited if desired. Another aspect of the plated electrode is that a continuous, fine-grained metallic film gives the full conductivity of the metal.

Plating ceramic objects calls for application of all the art and science of electrochemistry plus some techniques which are unique. For one thing, most ceramic bodies are excellent insulators so must be made conductive in some way prior to plating. Such conductivity is a surface effect, often discontinuous, and not a volume conductivity such as it is with metallic components.

Another problem arises from the relatively low density of ceramics compared with metals. This is not important when the components are racked but can plague mass production efforts that depend upon tumbling.

"Low Noise" Electrodes

One source of electrical noise is the result of discontinuities in the conductor. With some of the materials described in this paper, noise may be due to the insulating qualities of the ceramic binder. Aside from that, an additional source of noise comes from the point-to-point contacts of fairly large particles of metal. Chemically homogeneous and physically fine-grained metallic films are the answer to a reduction in noise level.

Electroplating over the conventional fired-on, glass bonded silver is one answer to a lower noise figure. An even better noise level can be obtained by first applying a fired-on, molecular precious metal coating such as that obtained with a gold decorating composition. Then the gold is electroplated with silver. A further heat-treatment will cause diffusion of one metal in the other.

Chemical Deposition of Silver

For over a hundred years mirrors have been made by depositing silver from a reduced ammoniacal solution. The same process can be the basis for developing conductive electrodes on other ceramic materials. A Government bulletin [3] gives detailed formulae and recommended procedures. These books on the subject of amateur telescope making [4, 5, 6] are invaluable references for refinements in techniques. And if you can read these interesting texts without wanting to run right down cellar and start grinding a telescope mirror, you are pretty thick skinned!

Surface Preparation Extremely Important

Surface preparation by cleaning and "sensitizing" is extremely important. Selective electrodes—for example, the insulating margins of tubular capacitors—can be obtained with stop-off lacquers. Ceramic sheets are simply immersed in the solution. Small tubes should be tumbled gently.

The silver film produced by these chemical methods is very thin, on the order of several millionths of an inch, so much be carefully handled. Directly after silvering the electrodes are built up to a substantial thickness of electroplating with copper or silver.

It would seem to be unnecessary to advise that a metal recovery program is requisite, yet it is not an uncommon practice for paint tools to be wiped with paper tissue and the tissue tossed away! Paint lost this way is charged up as a necessary expense of the operation. This can be prevented by instituting a paint recovery program and by providing containers for the collection of all silver waste.

Periodically the waste can be boxed and shipped to some company, such as Handy & Harman, that makes a business of reclamation. There the silver will be recovered and a payment made for the value of the silver minus nominal processing charges. It is usually best, though, to recover the metal locally, and then sell it to the metal refiner.

How To Prevent Tarnishing

As we all know, silver eventually tranishes due to sulphurous compounds in the atmosphere. Some communities are worse than others in this respect due to industrial "smog." Poor solderability is the principal trouble that accompanies tarnished surfaces. Of course, when the components are completely assembled right after forming the electrodes, there is nothing to fear from this source. The problem is mainly one of storing unsoldered units.

Happily, there is a simple, inexpensive, and completely effective solution. Merely put moth balls—yes, ordinary moth balls—in the storage containers. As long as the naphthalene remains, the silver will stay bright and untarnished. In glass containers, with tight fitting lids, this will be for years!

REFERENCES

1. Butts, Allison, and Thomas, J. M., "Corrosion Resistance of Silver and Silver Alloys," in Silver In Industry, edited by Lawrence Addicks, pp. 357–400, Reinhold Publishing Corp., New York (1940).
2. Zickrick, Lyall, "Silver In Stationary Electrical Contacts," in Silver In Industry, edited by Lawrence Addicks, pp. 298–299, Reinhold Publishing Corp., New York (1940).
3. Gardner, I. C., and Case, F. A., The Making of Mirrors By the Deposition of Metal On Glass. Circular of the Bureau of Standards No. 389, Superintendent of Documents, U. S. Government Printing Office, Washington, D. C. (1931). Price 10 cents.
4. Ingalls, Albert G., editor, Amateur Telescope Making (Book One), Scientific American, Inc., New York (4th ed., 12th printing, 1955).
5. Ingalls, Albert G., editor, Amateur Telescope Making (Book Two), Scientific American, Inc., New York (1st ed., 9th printing, 1954).
6. Ingalls, Albert G., editor, Amateur Telescope Making (Book Three), Scientific American, Inc., New York (1st ed., 1st printing, 1953).

CHAPTER XXVI

OXIDE CUTTING TOOLS

R. R. Van Der Beck, A. W. Von Mickwitz, L. G. Scheinman
Refractories Division, The Carborundum Co.

The successful application of oxide materials to the field of metal stock removal has been of very recent origin, notwithstanding the fact that the idea itself is not new. Review of the technical literature dealing with the subject shows that it dates back to the early 1900's. Recently, interest in oxide tools in the United States was created by the government's concern with the strategic role of tungsten in industrial and military applications. Through publicity developed by their project on oxide cutting tools, Watertown Arsenal interested private industry in conducting research on this problem.

Tools Gaining Acceptance

After a number of years of quite intensive work, considerable success was achieved and ceramic cutting tools have since been winning acceptance in the field of metal stock removal. This progress was made possible through the cooperative efforts of tool engineers and ceramic scientists. At the same time it is apparent to all concerned that the application of oxide cutting tools in the metal working industry is in its infancy and that many years will be required before the technology and economics of the application of such tools is fully known. Such was the case with carbide when they were first sold in competition with high speed steel.

Our organization feels that oxide will closely parallel the development of carbide in this field, achieving in time a proved position. We do not believe that oxide will replace carbide in every use any more than carbide replaced high speed steel. This picture, in which a gradual transition will occur as machines are improved to take full advantage of the superior performance which oxides offer in many applications, assumes that the United States does not become involved in any major war. If such an event occurred, the strategic nature of tungsten would greatly speed the evolution.

Barring such an unfortunate contingency, the problem at hand is to provide as smooth as possible a transition from the prototype phase of oxide tool development to their large scale use as manufacturing tools in areas where they have been shown to outperform other materials. This paper will be confined to a description of the physical properties of ceramic cutting tools and to their pertinent manufacturing processes.

Two Basic Firing Processes

In order to appreciate fully the properties of the various oxide cutting tools that are available at the present time, it is helpful to consider the fundamentals of the two basic firing processes by which ceramic tools may be manufactured. Until the present, most producers were reluctant to discuss this phase of their operations because of the possibility of divulging proprietary information to their competitors. At this date, however, competitors can judge with considerable accuracy the method of manufacture of a particular product, and there is no longer any reason to conceal this information from the public.

Oxide cutting tool materials are manufactured by variations of the preforming and sintering technique, or by use of the more recently developed hot pressing process. The term sintering is so fundamental that definition of the process is unnecessary. The term hot pressing, as it is popularly applied, refers to a technique whereby a loose material is pressed into shape at elevated temperature. It may be considered to be a special case of sintering in which the firing period is greatly reduced because of the application of pressure during the heating cycle. An induction furnace is usually employed.

The hot pressing process for the manufacture of cutting tools was adopted only after careful study had established that a high capital investment was justified by the inherent advantages of the process.

View of typical equipment used to hot press oxide tools at the Refractories Division of the Carborundum Co.

Physical Properties

If one considers the conditions to which cutting tools are exposed, including very high stresses, thermal shock, impact and vibration, he will certainly agree that this is a critical application for any material. Among ceramic materials, only aluminum oxide seems able to provide the required physical properties. This is probably due to the fact that aluminum oxide retains its excellent physical properties to temperatures at which most other materials decrease rapidly in strength. The literature indicates that the strength of alumina bodies probably increases with temperature.*

Experience has shown that microstructure is closely related to performance in an oxide cutting tool. One tool may exhibit superior performance characteristics, while a second tool which has the same composition, hardness and density, may show poor life in a cutting test. Complete control of this product can, therefore, be accomplished only by microstructure studies and cutting tests. In our opinion this fact was not fully appreciated until recently and is the cause of most of those difficulties which have been experienced in applying these materials. Microstructure may be regulated by the incorporation of controlled amounts of additives and by control of the firing cycle.

Crystallites Uniform in Size

For mechanical uses, such as are encountered in cutting applications, it is desirable to keep the individual crystallites as uniform in size and as small as possible, preferably less than 10 microns in size. Under practical forming conditions, the individual crystals tend to develop a very high degree of orientation because of the effect of temperature gradient during hot pressing. In this material, and under the conditions of our manufacture, temperature gradient usually appears to favor the growth of the crystals along the C axis.

In sintering this effect is not as pronounced, although it may occur. Orientation seems to be undesirable only if crystal growth is sufficient to affect close packing. In fact, preferential orientation appears to explain to some degree the superiority of hot pressed tools. The orientation is shown by parallel extinction which occurs when the specimen is rotated under the petrographic microscope using crossed nicols and a selenite plate. In such bodies, orientation of the individual alpha alumina crystals may prevent the development of mechanical stresses which would otherwise occur on cooling.

Where conventional sintering is employed, it is usually necessary to add impurities to produce a glassy phase and to lower the maturation temperature. The glass also provides an ideal environment for the growth of the alumina crystals. The crystals which develop are tubular in shape and may

---

* J. Hinnuber, "Oxide-Ceramic Cutting Tools in Comparison to Carbide," Fried, Krupp Widia—Fabrick, Essen (Germany). Industrie-Anzeiger, 71/72, 7 Sept. 1956, 1082-84.

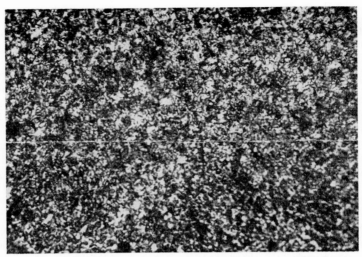

Microstructure of a typical oxide cutting tool material showing very uniform crystallites which average approximately five microns in diameter.

Lapmaster lapping machine showing assembled and partially assembled specimen holders. The felt pad equalizes the pressure on the specimens.

become several hundred microns or more across the larger dimension. The glassy phase, as well as their large size, prevents close association of the alumina crystals. It may also prevent an interlocking effect which is found in those hot pressed bodies which exhibit exceptional toughness and strength.

Strength at Elevated Temperatures

As stated earlier, one of the most valuable properties of aluminum oxide in applications involving exposure to mechanical stresses is its ability to maintain strength to elevated temperatures. Values obtained on a body prepared in our laboratory are shown in Table 1. This set was made using a Dillon Tensile Tester on specimens with a cross section of 0.166″ x 0.166″ and a span of one inch. This cross section was used because it conforms

TABLE I

Modulus of rupture of ceramic A

104,800 lbs./in.^{2}	
85,300	
111,500	
104,800	average 100,500 lbs./in.^{2}
98,300	
98,300	

closely with a standard thickness of cutting tool. The strength of carbide tools at room temperature is, of course, much higher than this, but the metal bond in carbide deteriorates in strength rather rapidly with increasing temperature.

One of the most important properties that a cutting tool must possess is abrasion resistance. Unfortunately, no one has fully succeeded in relating the physical properties of materials to their ability to withstand abrasion. For this reason it is necessary to measure this complex property. A material which performs very well in one abrasion test, for example, may fail badly in a different test purporting to measure the same property. The authors recently consulted a manual describing mechanical properties and tests and failed to find abrasion resistance listed.

Qualitative Test

Rather than sidestep the issue simply because of the difficulty in correlating the various methods of measuring this property, our laboratory devised a simple qualitative test using a Lapmaster lapping machine. This machine is commonly used on hard materials. The cover forces the samples down against the steel face of the lap, while an abrasive slurry is fed through a pumping system onto the lap. Boron carbide suspended in kerosene was used for these tests. The results of one representative test of Stupalox bodies and commercial carbide tool bodies using the Lapmaster is shown in Table 2. Reproducibility on this test is good, but the results are

TABLE II
Abrasion resistance of aluminum oxide vs. cemented carbide

	Volume per square inch of wearing surface
Carbide A	0.30
Carbide B	0.22
Carbide C	0.23
Oxide A	0.64
Oxide B	0.33
Oxide C	0.65
Oxide D	0.87

considered to be qualitative only. The results of this test indicate that oxide bodies are relatively abrasion resistant.

With but a few exceptions, ceramic tools are composed predominantly of alpha alumina crystals. The balance of the body is composed of additives which have been made to lower maturation temperature, control crystal size or impart a characteristic color. These additives naturally influence the microstructure of the bodies, including the type, shape, size and orientation of the crystals. Chrome oxide is a favorite in certain circles since it is refractory, forms a complete solid solution series with Al_2O_3, and imparts a distinctive pink color when added in quantities as low as 1% or less. In larger quantities it produces a dark, almost black body.

View of carbide and oxide cutting tool inserts at end of test. The cutting point of the oxide insert which was used in this test (at 9 o'clock) shows almost no wear, while a welded chip is shown on the carbide insert. In production, the eroded area on the ceramic tool (8 o'clock) which is the result of chip flow, could have been avoided by improved chip control.

Variations in Composition

It is interesting to note that the manufacturers of oxide tools generally do not offer a variety of oxide compositions for the reason that their present bodies achieve good results in most cases. There is some indication at present, however, that variations in composition will provide improved cutting properties, but not necessarily provide "grades" for various applications.

This is, of course, the significant relationship, the one to which we must relate the physical properties of both work and tool. It is also the area in which tool engineers and ceramists alike must look to different disciplines if the underlying relationships are to be defined.

One of the most significant differences between oxide and carbide tools is in the heat which is transferred to the tool during cutting. The practical consequence of the difference in temperature which results is that carbide tools must be metal bonded to the tool shank, while oxide tools operated under similar conditions may be bonded to the shank with epoxy resins. This is an observable fact, but it is disturbing that our knowledge to date is not sufficient to explain the phenomenon.

Thermal Conductivity

Some authorities have suggested that the difference in thermal conductivity is sufficient to explain the large difference in operating temperature. This differs by a factor of only two at room temperature, however, which does not seem adequate to explain the observed difference. Unless

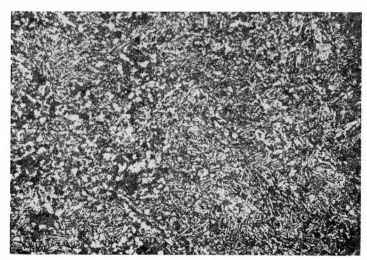

Representative microstructure of SAE 4140 bar stock (magnification 200x).

there are radical changes in relative conductivity values at operating temperatures, one must look to another explanation.

It appeared that a study of chip microstructure might shed some light on this problem, especially since it has been observed that there is a significant difference in color between the chips formed by the oxide and those formed by carbide tools generally show a more heavily oxidized surface than those formed by oxide tools under the same conditions of operations. This indicates that more energy was expended in the case of chips formed using carbide.

The study consisted of an examination of turnings made from a bar of SAE 4140 steel, using a carbide throwaway insert and a ceramic tool of the same size and geometry. Cutting conditions were:

0.050 inch depth of cut
0.0156 inch feed per revolution
Speed 734 S.F.P.M.

The cutting point of the oxide insert used in the test showed almost no wear, while a welded chip appeared in the carbide insert. In production, an eroded area on the ceramic tool, the result of chip flow, could have been avoided by improved chip control.

The study consisted of metallographic examination of the polished cross section of turnings produced by each tool, along with a section of the bar stock. The general microstructure of the bar stock denoted a quenched and tempered heat treatment. This is typical of the major portion of the structure. However, ideal homogeneity was not achieved and a condition known as "banding" was apparent.

Study Flow Lines

Our examination was primarily directed toward determining whether any detectable difference could be observed in the flow lines of the two chips. As indicated in the literature,[†] the microstructure of a chip will reveal flow lines which show the nature of shear and plastic strain to which the metal was subjected. Shear is defined as primary or secondary. Primary or internal shear is reported to occur when the metal is compressed beyond its elastic limit causing plastic deformation.

Flow lines which illustrate this phenomenon generally form a large angle with the base of the chip. Essentially all of the heat generated by this process is carried away by the chip. On the other hand, secondary shear is produced by the friction of the chip and tool interface, and, according to the literature, the heat generated remains at the tool surface. It is this friction and heat which is responsible for tool cratering, welding of chip and tool, and the rapid breakdown of carbide tools due to excessive temperature. Evidence of secondary shear can be observed in the chip

---

[†] A. B. Albrecht, Bulletin of the Monarch Machine Tool Co., Sidney, Ohio. Reprinted from American Machinist.

Microstructure of chip turned with carbide insert showing primary shear (top 2/3 of print) and secondary shear (bottom 1/3).

Microstructure of chip turned with oxide cutting tool insert showing primary shear (top 2/3 of print) and secondary shear (bottom 1/3).

microstructure by the change in the slope of the flow lines as they reach the base of the chip.

Amount of Secondary Shear

It was believed that, since an oxide tool remains relatively cool at all times, the answer might lie in the degree of secondary shear created by the two tool materials. In samples turned with both ceramic and carbide tools, however, the flow lines in the secondary shear region run parallel to the base of the chip. This would indicate that the amount of secondary shear was similar in both cases.

In this test there appeared to be no substantial difference in the secondary shear in chips turned with carbide and oxide tools and the explanation of the low operating temperature of oxide tools is still unresolved.

As with all ceramic materials, aluminum oxide bodies are subject to failure when exposed to severe tensile or impact stresses. Tool and tool holder must, therefore, be designed to provide uniform loading of the tool. Specifications on oxide tools are rather close, for example, in respect to parallelness of faces so that tensile stresses will not be developed in throwaway inserts during clamping. The bodies are also sensitive to thermal shock, which should be avoided when possible.

Conclusions

In conclusion, therefore, it is apparent that there is now available a new ceramic material which is superior in many respects to carbide in its usefulness in severe mechanical applications such as are encountered in cutting tools. Factors which contribute to the usefulness of the oxide tool are as follows:

1. The raw materials used in the manufacture of oxide cutting tools are more readily available and are of less strategic importance than the tungsten used in carbide tools.

2. Oxide tools retain their high strength, hardness and wear resistance at elevated temperatures, and thus tend to give longer life, cleaner cutting action, closer dimensional control and freedom from build-up or welding at the cutting edge during machining.

3. Oxide cutting tools frequently produce a finer surface finish than other tools, and may, therefore, replace grinding operations in many instances.

4. Machining time and costs are often significantly reduced because of the higher cutting speeds that are possible with oxide cutting tools.

CHAPTER XXVII

CERMET DEVELOPMENT

V. D. FRECHETTE
Alfred University

That ceramics and metals have been separated in our thinking is emphasized by the common definition of ceramic products as those produced from inorganic, *nonmetallic* raw materials at high temperatures, or destined for use at high temperatures. Nevertheless, from the beginning the metallurgist has been forced into the necessity to look towards ceramics for his crucibles, for the lining of his furnaces and ladles, and for his soaking pits and heat treating furnaces.

And if he has been blessed by the availability of ceramic products to answer these needs, he has occasionally been embarrassed by ceramic materials in another form when inclusions of nonmetallic types found their way into his metals to impair their working properties and the ease with which they could be machined.

Ceramists Look to Metals

For their part, ceramic technologists from earliest times have looked to metals for the base material on which to apply their enamel. They have used metallic gold, silver, and copper to decorate their artistic wares, and they have precipitated colloidal metallic gold from glass to produce their beautiful ruby ware. In more recent years, wire mesh has been pressed into glass to reinforce it, steel plates have been used to set basic brick in rotary kilns and steel furnaces, ceramic-coated heating elements have been developed for electric stoves, and high tension insulators have been metalized to reduce radio interference.

In the meantime the metallurgist has produced metal-bonded carbides for wear-resistant applications and to tip cutting tools. Goldschmidt's thermit process, involving a reaction between aluminum and a reducible oxide, has become familiar in every elementary chemistry text. Though the product of the thermit reaction was a mixture of metal and alumina, the presence of alumina in the product was accepted only as incidental and uninteresting.

For all the common ground of the metallurgist and the ceramist, the potentialities of the mixed metal-ceramic went unrealized until very recent years.

Early Experiments

Perhaps the first to suggest the possible value of such a metal-ceramic powder for high-temperature application was H. G. Schurecht at Alfred, who experimented in 1937 with spraying molten metals on ceramics. In that same year he mixed aluminum powder with clay and applied the coating to fireclay refractories noting the greatly improved slag resistance of the coated brick. He observed no such improvement when aluminum oxide was used instead of aluminum in compounding the coating.

This was followed in the years between 1937 and 1940 with other experiments on combinations of aluminum powder in the formulation of fireclay refractory brick, magnesite-chrome brick, silicon-carbide refractories, forsterite brick, and graphite crucibles. He recorded the generally high strength of such aluminum-ceramic products and their exceptional volume stability.

Curiously enough, the Alfred work attracted little attention and it was not until the closing years of World War II that the German development of iron-alumina compositions for jet aircraft stimulated a general interest in metal-ceramic compositions. An extraordinary sense of urgency in their development grew out of the new and stringent requirements imposed by the operating conditions in rockets and jet engines so that it has been estimated that there are over fifty industrial corporations, thirteen government agencies, three research foundations, and over twenty universities in the United States alone undertaking research and development in what has come to be called the cermet field, and work in other countries is on a proportionately high scale.

What Is A Cermet?

As a consequence of our present fragmentary knowledge of cermets, a definitive review of cermet technology is not yet possible. Perhaps a cermet may be defined as a ceramic body or coating in which an internal metal phase forms an essential part of the final composition or plays an essential role in the thermal maturing process.

Experiments with the German iron-alumina cermet and with similar compositions have led to the development of a chromium-alumina cermet by Blackburn. Electrolytic chromium and alpha-alumina are milled with tungsten carbide balls in alcohol. During this process contaminants of iron, tungsten, cobalt, silicon and manganese are picked up, but they are not considered objectionable.

Fabricating Process

The ware is fabricated by pressing in harden steel dies, removed from the mold, inclosed in a rubber envelope and is subjected to a hydrostatic pressure of 2400 kilograms per square centimeter. Sintering is accomplished in purified hydrogen in the presence of titanium hydride, yielding a product in which a small percentage of chromic oxide is dissolved in the corundum phase, while the chromium remains as the metal. The firing shrinkage during this process amounts to about 15 percent to yield a completely dense product with a specific gravity of 5.9 and a modulus of elasticity of 47.2×10^6. The impact resistance and thermal shock resistance are reported to be very good. Oxidation during service is very slow and the modulus of rupture is high.

Numerous other metal-oxide combinations have been tested, but none have been reported as having as much promise as the chromium-alumina cermet for high temperature service.

A great many carbide-metal cermets have been produced and tested, including those employing cobalt, nickel, chromium, iron, ferrosilicon, niobium, and silicon alone or in combinations as the metal phase, and titanium carbide, silicon carbide, boron carbide, zirconium carbide, columbium carbide, tantalum carbide and tungsten carbide have been used as the ceramic phase.

Simple metal-bonded carbides, such as nickel-bonded titanium carbide or cobalt-carbide tungsten carbide, are produced industrially by wet ball milling. The mixture is formed by pressing or extruding, followed if necessary by hydrostatic pressing, and are then sintered in hydrogen or vacuum furnaces.

Hot Pressing Method

Another carbide-metal cermet is described by Lidman and Hamjian, who prepared zirconium carbide-niobium mixtures by hot pressing. During the process an exchange reaction occurred by which niobium carbide was formed and dissolved in the zirconium carbide while zirconium metal was freed to concentrate at the grain corners of the carbide. They found that a fine dispersion of the zirconium metal phase was most favorable to high strength, while an increase in the temperature or time of firing caused coalescence of the zirconium and reduced the cold strength.

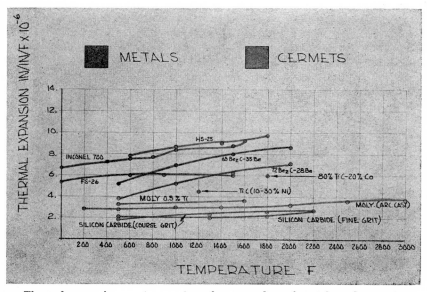

Thermal expansion vs. temperature for a number of metals and cermets.

A pure carbide was formed by Foster and others who explored the use of fugitive metal binders such as cobalt or nickel in small percentages.

Silicon carbide pieces of exceptionally high density have been produced at Alfred by application of the Hedvall effect. Beta silicon carbide is prepared by heating pure silicon and carbon. The product is cleaned by acid and water flotation and formed into ware by hot-pressing.

Carbide Body Experiments

A recent paper from Ohio State University reports experiments with multiple carbide bodies. Mixtures of boron carbide, titanium carbide and silicon carbide, were wet-milled, formed by pressing and followed by hydrostatic pressing and sintering. Specimens were also formed satisfactorily by hot-pressing. By either method of fabrication specimens of almost zero porosity and exceptionally good oxidation resistance resulted. The product was still further improved by introducing silicon and boron as the elements instead of the carbides.

At Alfred, Tinklepaugh and his co-workers have added molybdenum and silicon in small amounts to titanium carbide-chromium and titanium carbide-iron cermets in order to make them self-glazing, that is, so that the oxidation products form an impervious protective coating. Wilson chose another approach describing application of a coating to a titanium carbide-cobalt cermet by dipping it in a slip consisting of chrominum-barium silicate. The resulting coating was extremely effective in protecting the body against oxidation at temperatures as high as 1200° C., and was not damaged by thermal shock nor cracked by temperature creep of the piece.

Aided by Fundamental Research

The efforts to develop useful cermets are being supported also by research of a more fundamental nature on the underlying principles of sintering mechanisms, metal-ceramic wetting and bonding, chemical reactions between components, diffusion between components and products and the mechanism of deterioration and destruction under the conditions of service by oxidation, corrosion, mechanical stresses, and thermal shock.

In general, the sintering process has proved to be subject to the same laws as have already been stated by Hedvall and others as controlling solid state reactions of all types.

Kingery at the Massachusetts Institute of Technology has noted the obscurity in which the whole question of the wetting and bonding of metals to ceramics lies, and has undertaken a series of investigations designed to throw light on this problem. He and his collaborators have studied the interfacial relationships existing in forty-two metal-oxide pairs and have recorded four general types of behavior.

In studies of surface tension and wetting in metal-ceramic systems, they observed that both the metal and the ceramic affect the wetting tendency and the work of adhesion. By calculation of the interfacial energies involved, they were able to explain the action of small additions of silicon to iron in having little effect on the surface tension of the iron, but a profound effect on the interfacial relationships of the iron with alumina. No perferential concentration of silicon was found to occur at the free iron surface but the silicon did concentrate at the iron-alumina interface, probably because the silicon-oxygen bond is so much stronger than the iron oxygen bond.

Employs Radioactive Isotopes

Crandall and his colleagues at Alfred have been studying the diffusion of iron, cobalt and nickel into hot-pressed titanium carbide, using radioactive isotopes as tracers, the oxidation mechanisms of oxide-metal and carbide-metal cermets, and the effects of porosity, metal concentration, temperature, and oxidation state on the process. They have also been investigating the mechanism of thermal shock failure with signal success.

Not a little of the effort on high temperature cermet development has gone into the development of test methods for evaluating the products, including the creep, tensile strength, modulus of rupture, and modulus of elasticity at high temperatures, and the resistance to impact, to thermal shock, to oxidation and to corrosion under simulated service conditions.

Develop Fabrication Techniques

Other projects have been directed towards the development of fabrication techniques including hydrostatic pressing to obtain dense and uniform compacts prior to sintering. Hot pressing has received special attention with regard to the design of graphite dies to permit high pressures and to the control of temperature under the conditions of heating by high frequency induction, by furnace resistance and by the resistance of the charge itself. The molten casting of ceramic-metal compositions melted by induction heating with violent agitation is being attempted.

Little has been done to exploit the possibility of developing favorable internal stresses between the phases of the body and the distribution of stresses from place to place in the ware, perhaps with the aid of composition gradients, in order to meet the strength requirements for such specific applications as turbine elements. Until very recently there has been little done also to develop layered, laminated or fibered body textures, although the success of the well-known oriented graphite-silver compacts used in electrical contactors suggests that such structures may be worth study.

The subject of cermets can scarcely be said to have been even opened by these few years of experimentation. Yet the art is growing, and already the quality of some of the cermet products establishes this family of materials as one of the most significant in our technology. The future of our industrial economy must certainly be linked with them in proportion to our increasing demands for high temperature structural materials, for more efficient and more precise cutting tools and so on.

Other Important Applications

There has been time to deal only with cermets in their high temperature aspects here, but their other applications should at least be remembered by a glance at a few listed recently by Westbrook. These include lamp filaments, gas turbine parts, rocket engine components, contact materials, magnets, cutting and grinding tools, metal-ceramic vacuum seals, friction parts, abrasion-resistant parts, sparkplug bodies, electrodes, nuclear power applications, thermoelectric generators, liquid metal pumps, heating elements, resistors, and bearings.

The technology of cermets is evidently complex. But if the difficulties seem great, so are the future prospects for this new and lively branch of the ceramics field.

CHAPTER XXVIII

RAW MATERIALS FOR ELECTRONIC CERAMICS

ALUMINA. Of all the new ceramic materials, alumina probably has the widest diversity of uses and the greatest potentialities. Its outstanding mechanical strength, excellent thermal shock resistance, excellent thermal shock resistance, excellent electrical properties (high dielectric strength, low power factor, etc.) and its chemical and abrasion resistance, make it well suited to a variety of aplications.

The war-time demand for high-alumina porcelain, especially for use in aircraft insulators, has brought forth a wide variety of such ware as well as many patents covering compositions and manufacturing methods. Substantially all automotive spark plugs today contain at least 85% alumina in the composition. One company in the United States mixes Bayer alumina with a few percent of fluxing materials and powdered phenolformaldehyde resin, and then forms insulators to shape by hot compression molding. These are burned at about 1700° C. Another method described by the same company is to form the mixture of thermoplastic resin, fluxes and fine ground alumina by injection molding in multiple cavity dies. In either case the organic additive must be burned out completely, whereupon the body shrinks to a nonporous condition. Another company wet-grinds dense Bayer alumina to carefully controlled size distribution, blends in the fluxing ingredients, spray-dries a suspension of the insulator composition to obtain a free-flowing pelletized feed to rubber molds which are compressed isostatically to form. Insulator blanks may also be formed by extrusion and profiled to the desired shape in the moist or dry condition. In most production methods some grinding or diamond lathe-tool work is necessary to meet rigid dimensional tolerances. The main virtues of the high-alumina porcelains for spark plug use are: high electrical resistivity at elevated temperatures, high impact strength, good thermal conductivity, and good resistance to thermal shock.

Uses for high alumina ceramics include electronic tube parts, ceramic-to-metal seals, high frequency insulators, holders and spacers for printed circuits, radomes and missile nose cones.

Mechanical uses for high alumina bodies include seal surfaces for mechanical rotary seals for pumps and similar equipment, plungers or liners in reciprocating pumps, nozzles, rock bits, cutting tools, non-lubricated hi-temperature roller bearings, and a wide variety of other mechanical parts.

High alumina ceramics are fired ceramic compositions in which the major crystal phase is alpha alumina or corundum. The aluminum oxide content is usually 75 to 100% and the parts are fired at temperatures ranging from 2600° F. to 3200° F., or higher, on a commercial scale. Material is available in both the vitrified and porous forms, with the 100% (or nearly 100%) aluminum oxide compositions most commonly being used in

PHYSICAL PROPERTIES OF HIGH ALUMINA CERAMICS

Property	Unit	85% Al$_2$O$_3$ Vit. Body	95% Al$_2$O$_3$ Vit. Body	99.5+Al$_2$O$_3$ Vit. Body	99.5+Al$_2$O$_3$ Porous Body
Tensile Strength	Psi	17-23000	25-35000	37500-38000	-----
Compressive Strength	Psi	140,-400,000	250,-400,000	427,000	10-125000
Flexural Strength	Psi	30-45000	45-50000	42700-47000	10-22000
Modulus of Elasticity	Psi	31-35 x 10^6	39-43 x 10^6	52 x 10^6	-----
Impact Resistance	Inch-Pounds Charpy	5.8-7.0	6.2-7.6	-----	3.0
Specific Gravity	-----	3.40-3.53	3.61-3.75	3.7-3.97	2.4-3.40
Water Absorption	Per cent	0.00-.02	0.00	0.00	7-1.8
Porosity	Per cent	<1 Gas Tight*	<1 Gas Tight*	<1	7¼ -----
Hardness	Moh's Scale Knoop	8.5-9 1450	9 1720	9 -----	----- -----
Maximum Working Temperature	°C °F	1300-1400 2200-2550	1600-1700 2910-3100	1950 3542	1400-1800 2550-3270
Pore Size	Microns	-----	-----	-----	2-3
Specific Heat	BTU per lb. BTU/hr/ft²/100° BTU/hr/ft²/800°	0.180 90-116 180	0.188-0.190 130-150 240	0.22 135 -----	----- 116 -----

* Helium mass spectrometer test on 0.010" sections

Property	Unit	85%	95%	99.5 Vit	99.5 Porous
Thermal Conductivity	°F/in. — 1600°	230	300	-----	-----
Thermal Coefficient of Expansion °C	25-200° 25-600 25-700 25-800 25-1000	5.47-5.68 x 10^{-6} 6.55-6.96 7.6-7.9 7.33 7.67-7.89	5.7-6.67 x 10^{-6} 6.7-7.65 8.07 7.6 8.45-9.14	----- ----- 7.7 ----- 8.4	5.1 x 10^{-6} ----- ----- ----- -----
Thermal Shock Resistance		Fair	Good	Good	Good
Dielectric Strength Volts/mil	AC 25°C. 500°C. 1000°C.	205-350 ----- -----	250-400 100-120 20-30	380 ----- -----	50 ----- -----
Volume Resistivity ohms/cm²	25°C. 100°C. 200° 300°C. 400°C. 500°C. 600°C. 700°C. 800°C. 900°C.	1-3.6 x 10^{14} 2-7.5 x 10^{13} ----- 1-5.0 x 10^{10} ----- 1 x 10^8-7.5 x 10^9 ----- 3-7.0 x 10^6 ----- 4-5.0 x 10^5	10^{16} 9.0 x 10^{14} 10 x 10^{13} 5.3 x 10^{12} 10 x 10^{10} 1.2-4.5 x 10^{10} 10^8 6.0 x 10^8 ----- -----	----- ----- ----- 1.2 x 10^{13} ----- 1.3 x 10^{11} ----- ----- 3.5 x 10^6 -----	10^{14} 8.5 x 10^{13}-1 x 10^{14} ----- 1 x 10^{10}-1.5 x 10^{11} ----- 7.5 x 10^7-1.0 x 10^9 ----- 3.6 x 10^6-3.0 x 10^7 ----- 5.6 x 10^5
Te VALUE °C		750⟩1000	800⟩1100	1100	835⟩1100

the porous form. Alumina ceramics can be glazed when maintaining surface cleanliness is a requirement, and are readily metallized.

There are several commercial grades of alumina powder available in regular or tabular form. Alumina is also available in the fused grain form for high purity applications, electronic applications, etc. Also used in a variety of cermet compositions and flame sprays as a coating.

Properties—As compared to other ceramic materials, alumina ceramics are superior mainly in regard to strength, impact resistance and hardness, as illustrated by table I.

The hardness of aluminum oxide compositions, making them suitable for abrasion resistant applications, cutting tools, etc., is greater than many materials normally considered hard, as shown by table II.

Resistance to Temperature—High alumina bodies are extremely temperature resistant depending upon the percentage of alumina present, and upon their original firing temperature. 95% alumina bodies retain their full tensile strength at temperatures up to and sometimes above 2000° F., and retain good portions of the tensile strength at even higher temperatures.

For many of the mechanical and some of the electrical applications of alumina, isostatic or hydrostatic pressing is used. Blanks are initially produced by pressing dry unfired powder in a rubber sack or mold under high hydraulic pressure. Uniform compaction and homogeneity are obtained by this application of uniform pressure from all directions and a true and accurate inside contour can be formed by pressing the powder around a metal arbor or mandrel. The outside shape is formed by machining the pressed blanks.

Fired parts, although extremely hard, can be ground by diamond wheels or diamond tools and tolerances of plus or minus 0.001 inch are readily obtainable. By using lapping technique tolerances of plus or minus one ten-thousandths of an inch are also obtainable, but the cost involved is relatively high.

In high temperature coatings, alumina is added to increase refractoriness. A typical coating would have the following composition :

Hard member (commercial frit)	50 lbs.
Soft member (commercial frit)	50 lbs.
Calcined alumina	50 lbs. (or more)
Black label clay	5 lbs.
Red label clay	5 lbs.
Cobalt oxide	1 lb.
Borax	4 oz.
Citric acid crystals	22 grams
Water	6 gal.

Fusion of the low temperature ground coat frit protects the metal from excessive oxidation at elevated temperatures, while the alumina aids in the formation of a refractory, heat-resistant coating.

Coatings of this type resist combustion products and minimize oxidation

ELECTRICAL PROPERTIES OF HIGH ALUMINA CERAMICS

Property		Vit. 85% 25°C.	500°C.	Vit. 95% 25°C.	500°C.	Vit. 99.5+%	Porous 99.5+%
Dielectric Constant	60 cycle	8.4		9.2			
	1×10^3 (1 kc)	7.65- 8.75	13.86	8.84- 10.51	13.3	10	
	1×10^6 (1 mc)	7.4- 8.95	8.87	8.81 9.60	9.03		5.5
	1×10^8	8.10- 8.95		8.80 9.60			5.3
	1×10^9			8.60			
	3×10^9	8.14		8.80			
	1×10^{10}	8.08- 8.77	8.26	8.40- 9.36	9.03		7.07
Power Factor Tan δ	60 cycle	.0013- .0015		.0005			
	1×10^3	.0002- .0014	0.580	.00007- .0006	1.1		
	1×10^6	.0007- .0012	.024	.00035- .0035	.012		.0005
	1×10^8	.0009		.00035- .0040	---		.0005
	1×10^9	----		.0006			
	3×10^9	.0014		.0010			
	1×10^{10}	.0027	.0033	.0008- .0015	.0021		
Loss Factor	60 cycle	.011- .013-					
	1×10^3	.00175- .0115	8.0	.0008- .0053	14.6		
	1×10^6	.0018- .0078	.21	.0014 .0035	.108		.003
	1×10^8	.006- .0074		.0031- .0040			.003
	1×10^9	.0076		.0038			
	3×10^9	.0114		.0088			
	1×10^{10}	.013- .0218	.027	.0067 .0140	.019		.00075

TABLE I

	Tensile strength (psi)	Charpy impact resistance (in.-lbs.)	Hardness Moh's scale
Alumina	13,000 to 38,000	5.8 to 7.5	9
Zircon	10,000 to 16,000	5.5	8.0
Sillimanite	11,000 to 14,000	5.5	7.5–8.0
Steatite	5,000 to 15,000	4.0 to 5.0	7.5
Forsterite	10,000	4.0	7.5
Elec. Porc.	2,400 to 8,000	4.0	6.5–7.0

in a temperature range of 1000° to 1400° F. and are used on jet aircraft combustion liners, compressor blades and tank mufflers, as well as exhaust pipes for trucks.

A type of hot pressing in which the alumina is mixed with a small amount of powdered resin and injected into heated molds is also used. The resin burns out during firing. Using this molding technique in a graphite mold, densities of 3.98 have been obtained.

Alumina cutting tools made by this hot pressing technique show the following physical characteristics:

```
Specific Gravity............................... 3.95
Porosity....................................... Zero
Thermal Conductivity
    Btu/hr/°F./ft/ft²......................... 18.
    g-cal/sec/°C./cm/cm²...................... .056
Coefficient of Thermal Expansion
    20° C. to 500°C........................... 7 x 10⁻⁶/°C.
    68° F. to 932° F.......................... 3.9 x 10⁻⁶/°F.
Modulus of Elasticity (70° C.)................ 60 x 10⁶ psi
Trans. Rupture Strength (70° C.).............. to 100,000 psi
Compressive Strength.......................... to 450,000 psi
Hardness—Rockwell A-93........................ 96.5
```

TABLE II

Material	Knoop hardness factor*	Moh's scale
Diamond	6,000–6,500	10
Boron carbide	2,300–2,800	
Silicon carbide	2,000–2,500	
Sapphire (pure corundum)	1,800–2,000	9
Alumina ceramics	1,400–1,750	
Tungsten carbide	1,050–1,900	
Topaz	1,250	8
H. S. steel	650–900	
Quartz	710–790	7

* Bureau of standards tests and R. C. Brewer.

High temperature sandwich type ceramic structures have been made using long-fiber asbestos paper, formed as square or hexagonal cores and dipped in alumina. These form a honeycomb, on the top and bottom of which a skin, made similarly, is applied, and the assembly fired to 3000° F. The firing burns out the paper and leaves a honeycomb alumina structure about 0.020″ thick. The fired structure can be machined and has a compressive strength up to 30,000 psi.

ALUMINUM ANTIMONIDE. AlSb. Mol. wt. 148.7. Melting Point 1080° C.

Crystallizes in zinc-blende structure. Crystals are hard, brittle, and metallic in appearance. Bonding is largely homopolar in character with some heteropolar contribution. Prepared by melting together pure aluminum and pure antimony in Al_2O_3 crucible under inert or reducing atmosphere. The solubility of either aluminum or antimony in the compound is minute or non-existent. Single crystals are prepared by the technique of withdrawing a seed crystal slowly from the surface of a melt of the material held just above the melting temperature. This method in necessitated by the fact that AlSb expands upon freezing.

AlSb is of interest as a semiconductor for electronic applications. Its electronic energy band gap, 1.6 ev is greater than that of silicon, thus offering the possibility of its application for rectifiers and transistors at temperatures higher than presently attainable. The mobility of the positive carriers is about 450 cm^2/volt-sec, which is about the same as that of silicon. However, the electron mobility of 250 cm^2/volt-sec is considerably lower.

BARIUM CARBONATE. Many steatite formulations have higher dielectric properties with an addition of barium carbonate. The material is used as a flux and a replacement for feldspar. Barium carbonate is used in making hard core types of permanent magnets. About 18% of barium carbonate is used in typical barium ferrite mixes for these applications.

BARIUM STANNATE. Barium stannate, as prepared by precipitation from an aqueous reaction, is a white powder, having the formula: $BaSnO_3 \cdot 3H_2O$. The hydrated compound loses its water by dehydration upon heating to 280° C. or above, leaving the anhydrous barium stannate ($BaSnO_3$, M.W.—304.06). The anhydrous compound may also be prepared by calcination of a barium compound, e.g., $BaCO_3$ and SnO_2.

Barium stannate is used as an additive to barium titanate bodies for use as ceramic capacitors. The addition of barium stannate to barium titanate bodies produces a shift in the Curie peak (point of maximum dielectric constant in a graph of this property versus temperature) to lower temperatures, the amount of shift being a linear function of the molar addition. Bodies of very high dielectric constant at room temperature (K—8000–12,000) may be obtained with compositions consisting of approximately 91 mole percent $BaTiO_3$ and 9 mole percent $BaSnO_3$.

BARIUM TITANATE. $BaTiO_3$. A compound produced by the reaction of barium carbonate and titanium dioxide, which has widespread use in the electronics industry because of its high dielectric constant, piezoelectric properties and ferroelectric properties.

The high dielectric constant of barium titanate make it exceptionally suitable for miniature electronic and communication equipment, the demand for which rose greatly during World War II and has increased greatly since that time. Bulky capacitors have been replaced in many instances by smaller titanate capacitors. In addition, most condensers used today in electronic equipment such as television and radio receivers are ceramic types.

At present there is only one commercial grade of barium titanate used for dielectric purposes, although various laboratories, etc., have attempted to prepare very pure barium titanate for experimental studies, etc.

The effect of even small quantities of impurities upon the property of barium titanate makes it essential that once these materials are received, that every effort be made to keep them free from impurities, including keeping the silica and alumina pickup from the ball milling operation at a minimum.

In preparing barium titanate bodies for capacitors and other dielectric purposes, mixing is done by wet milling if two or more components are used. After dryng the body, it is micropulverized, tempered with about 8% water by weight, throughly mixed, and then granulated by forcing through a 20-mesh screen.

For pressing, pressures of about 10,000 lbs. per square inch are used, with a holding time of 5 seconds being common for disks .25 inch thick and one inch in diameter.

After drying, the formed disks or parts are placed in saggers which have been previously dusted with zirconium oxide powder.

Barium titanate bodies are fired to vitrification at temperatures of between 2400° F. to 2500° F., with a two-hour soak at peak temperature. Sticking together of discs during firing is a serious problem which is solved by various plants in a wide variety of ways.

Properties—The dielectric constant of barium titanate is 1350 to 1600 at 1 Mc (25° C.) with power factor at the same frequency and temperature being a maximum of 1.5%. The dielectric constant of barium titanate varies quite decidedly with the temperature.

Power factor of barium titanate varies decidedly with the temperature.

Below 200° C., the thermal expansion of barium titanate is not quite linear, but at higher temperatures becomes a linear function.

Effect of impurities—Even very small quantities of silica drastically lower the room temperature K of barium titanate cmpositions but have only a slight effect upon power factor at the same temperature. Silica additions also drastically lower the peak value of the dielectric constant.

The addition of alumina has much less effect upon titanate compositions than silica with about 2% alumina performing the same functions as $\frac{1}{2}$% silica.

Effect of varying the $BaO:TiO_2$ ratio—As the BaO is increased from a deficiency through the stoichiometric ratio to an excess, the dielectric constant at room temperature increases, the room temperature power factor also increases, and the Curie temperature decreases. Although the general shape of the dielectric constant curve is not affected, the effect upon power factor is pronounced. Another aspect of varying the BaO-TiO_2 stoichiometric ratio is that in high K bodies (excess BaO) aging is much more rapid (for a 1200 K body at room temperature this loss of dielectric constant may be as much as 5% in 10 days while for a 2000 K body the loss may be as high as 10% in 10 days).

BARIUM ZIRCONATE—$BaO \cdot ZrO_2$. Used primarily as an addition agent with barium titanate and other titanate or zirconate dielectric materials to obtain dielectric bodies with special electrical properties. Due to its refractory nature it is not used as a single component body. Normally used in the range of 8 to 10%, depending on balance of composition, producing bodies with dielectric constants ranging from 3000 to 7000 at the Curie temperatures.

BERYLLIUM OXIDE has come to the fore as an ingredient of steatite bodies, see J. A. Cer. S., Vol. 25, No. 15, having 20 parts kaolin, 80 parts steatite talc and 5.93 parts BeO. Body had a specific resistance at 350° C. of 1.1×10^{12} ohm/cm and a susceptance to conductance at 350° C. of 13 at 100kc and 25 at 3 mc.

Has extremely high thermal conductivity, 40 to 50 times that of electrical porcelain and approaching metallic aluminum in bodies containing 80% BeO maturing at 1500° C. (J. A. Cer. S. Vol. 33, No. 4). Compressive strengths in excess of 250,000 lbs./in.^{2} have been obtained in high BeO bodies. (R. P. 1703 National Bureau of Standards.)

BeO is being used in nuclear reactors because of its refractoriness, high thermal conductivity and its ability to act as a moderator for fast neutrons, reducing them to "thermal" speeds. "Thermal" neutrons are more efficient in causing the fusion of U^{235}.

BISMUTH OXIDE—Used as an ingredient in fluxes for fired-on types of conductive silver paints. Calcined bismuth oxide can be used by itself for a flux to bond metallic silver flake to ceramic bodies.

BISMUTH SELENIDE. Bi_2Se_3. Mol. wt. 654.9. Melting point 706° C. Crystal structure, rhombohedral. Bi_2Se_3 does not appear to be as promising as Bi_2Te_3 for thermoelectric applications. Some materials of the type $Bi_2(Te,Se)_3$ offer the advantage of a higher operating temperature without a serious loss in efficiency.

BISMUTH STANNATE. Bismuth stannate, a hydrated compound of the formula $Bi_2(SnO_3)_3 \cdot 5H_2O$, is a cream-colored powder prepared from an aqueous reaction. Complete dehydration takes place upon heating to 200° C. or above, leaving the compound $Bi_2(SnO_3)_3$ (M. W. −918.10).

Bismuth stannate is used as an additive to barium titanate ceramic capacitor compositions to produce bodies of intermediate level of dielectric constant (1000–1300) which show remarkably little variation with temperature. A body consisting of 5 mole percent $Bi_2(SnO_3)_3$ and 95 mole percent $BaTiO_3$, has a dielectric constant at 25° C. of 1000 and varies less than 3% over the temperature range from −60° C. to 85° C.

This dielectric is also characterized by a dissipation factor of less than 1% at 1 KC and 25° C. and by unusually long life, high insulation resistance and high dielectric strength at elevated temperatures.

BISMUTH TELLURIDE. Bi_2Te_3. Mol. wt. 800.98. The crystal structure is rhombohedral. Melting point 585° C. Bi_2Te_3 is usually prepared by reacting nearly stoichiometric amounts of the elements and allowing directional freezing to take place.

Bi_2Te_3 is the best known thermoelectric material at the present time. Because it loses its semiconducting properties above approximately 100° C., Bi_2Te_3 is being used only in cooling devices.

BORON CARBIDE. B_4C. A very hard, highly refractory material used both for abrasive and abrasion-resistant applications, special refractory parts (especially where abrasion resistance is required).

Boron carbide is presently available in two common grades: Technical— 67%–75% boron, bulk density, 1.8 to 2.3 grams per cubic centimeter; high purity—75%–80% boron, bulk density, 2.4 to 2.5 grams per cubic centimeter (hot pressed). (The theoretical boron content of pure boron carbide is 78.3% boron.)

Boron carbide is extremely hard (second only to diamond), has a melting point of 2450° C., and sublimes at 3000° C. It is strong as far as ceramic compositions go, having a bending strength of 40,000 psi and a compressive strength of 414,000 psi. Its thermal expansion is relatively low (45×10^{-8}), it has a thermal conductivity of .065 cgs (about two-thirds that of silicon carbide) and electrical resistivity of 0.3–0.8 ohm cm.

When formed into special shapes, either hot pressing, or cold moulding and sintering can be used. These two methods (self-bonding) provide the maximum melting point, resistance to chemical attack and physical strength.

For very intricate and highly special shapes, as well as for large shapes, the boron carbide can be bonded with carbon, fused sodium silicate or boron oxide and other silicates, borate frits, glass materials, metals or cermets or plastic or rubber materials, depending upon the temperature and other conditions of application. This method is less costly than the self-bonding technique, but, of course, seriously affects the properties of boron carbide.

As an abrasive, boron carbide is used for ultrasonic grinding and drilling, fine polishing, but not for bonded abrasive wheels.

Abrasion-resistant parts made from boron carbide include spray nozzles, bearing liners and furnace parts. Boron carbide's refractory properties are of value in addition to the abrasion resistance in the latter application. Boron carbide is chemically inert, although it will react with oxygen at higher temperatures, and with white hot or molten metals of the iron group and certain transition metals.

In the atomic energy field, boron carbide and elemental boron are used for nuclear reactor control elements, radiation shields, etc.

BORON NITRIDE. A very soft, unctuous highly refractory material resembling graphite, with excellent thermal insulation properties and chemical stability.

Boron nitride is available in a wide variety of grades, varying from the pure material, almost 44% boron (theoretical composition: 43.6% boron–56.4% nitrogen) down to very impure materials. The properties are very sensitive to impurities and chemical analysis of the material is very important.

Boron nitride is very soft, but has excellent refractory properties, such as a melting point (which is actually a point of sublimation) of 2730° C., excellent chemical stability (although it will react with oxygen at temperatures of 650° C. and above), and it is not wettable by most metals, glass cryolite or other materials.

A very low thermal conductivity makes boron nitride useful as a thermal insulator. In powdered form, the material is capable of maintaining a temperature gradient of over 2000° C., through a 1-inch thickness under high vacuum.

Some types of boron nitride powder may be hot-pressed into white, ivory-like, impermeable, machinable form, quite soft (2 on Mohs scale) but with extreme resistance to corrosion by fused salts, molten metals and oxides, and glasses and slags. Also very high in electrical resistivity over wide frequency range: from 17×10^{12} ohm-cm. at 75° F. to 3×10^4 ohm-cm. at 1800° F. Dielectric constant 4+ over wide temperature and frequency range. Thermal conductivity of dense hot-pressed BN fairly high, from 85 to 200 BTU/sq. ft./in./° F. Thermal expansion coefficient varies from 0.4 in./in./°F. $\times 10^{-6}$ perpendicular to molding pressure to 5 parallel to mold pressure. Has slight resiliency, imparting outstanding heat shock resistance and fair toughness.

Uses include crucibles, parts for chemical equipment and pumps, rocket nozzles, vacuum tube separators, seals and gaskets, and as a neutron absorber.

Boron nitride's nonwettability has also made it useful as a mold lubricant in glass manufacture.

A cubic form of BN has been made, which is hard enough to scratch diamond and has good electrical insulation and good thermal resistance.

CADMIUM ZIRCONATE. $CdO \cdot ZrO_2$. M. W. 251.4—Approximate analysis, 51.1% CdO and 48.9% ZrO_2. Used as an addition to barium titanate type capacitor formulations in amounts up to 10% by weight. Generally acts as a depressant of the dielectric constant at the Curie temperature.

CALCIUM CARBONATE. Precipitated calcium carbonate, in low micron sizes, is used as an inorganic filler in "basing cements." These cements consist of a two-stage phenol-formaldehyde resin, calcium carbonate filler and enough hexamethylene-tetramine to catalyze the reaction of the resin with heat. Sometimes varous organic dyes are added. Basing cements are used to attach vacuum tubes to their bases. The material can also be used as insulating coatings for ceramic capacitors and printed circuits.

CALCIUM STANNATE. Calcium stannate, as prepared by precipitation from an aqueous reaction, is a white powder, having the formula: $CaSnO_3 \cdot 3H_2O$. The hydrated compound loses its water of hydration upon heating to 350° C. or above, leaving the anhydrous calcium stannate ($CaSnO_3$, M. W. —206.78). The anhydrous compound may also be prepared by calcination of a calcium compound, e.g., $CaCO_3$, and SnO_2.

Calcium stannate is used as an additive to barium titanate capacitor bodies in which it acts similarly to barium stannate, when compared on a molar basis. (See under barium stannate.) Calcium stannate bodies mature more readily than do equivalent bodies using barium stannate. It has been suggested as a base for phosphors.

CALCIUM TITANATE. $CaO \cdot TiO_2$. Calcium Titanate is a high dielectric material which when fired as a single component body to maturity and tested at one kilocycle and one megacycle, has a dielectric constant in the range of 150 to 175, a power factor of less than 0.07%, a negative temperature coefficient of capacity of 1400. Firing temperatures are from 2450 to 2500° F.

The power factor of calcium titanate is fairly constant from —125 to 50° C., but increases sharply from 50° to 120° C. The dielectric constant decreases rapidly over the temperature range —125° to 120° C. Over the frequency range 10^2 to 10^7 c/s, the dielectric constant is stable, while the temperature range varies widely, following a U-shaped curve.

Calcium titanate compositions can be either dry pressed, or slip cast and are usually fired to vitrification at a peak temperature of 2300° to 2400° F. Other steps in the manufacturing operation are similar to those used for barium titanate.

Calcium titanate is a relatively dense material (3.17 grams per cc in powder form, 4.02 grams per cc in fired form) and has a linear thermal expansion in the range of —70° to over 150° C.

To form high K bodies, calcium titanate is used as a single component or is blended with barium titanate and other alkali earth zirconates and/or titanates. It is also used as an addition to barium titanate for piezoelectric bodies. Also used in conjunction with barium titanate-lead titanate piezoelectric bodies. Three to five percent calcium titanate is normally used.

CALCIUM ZIRCONATE. $CaO \cdot ZrO_2$. Is used primarily in the dielectric field as an addition agent with titanate bodies to obtain bodies with special electrical properties. Used in the range of three to 10%.

CELLULOSE NITRATE. A temporary binder for some conductive coatings and the basis for many lacquers, protective coatings, color code paints, etc.

CERMETS. Titanium carbide base, alumina-chromium and thoria-molybdenum cermets are listed.

Titanium carbide cermets are made by ballmilling TiC plus nickel or cobalt down to 2 to 5 micron grain size. With 2% of temporary wax binder, they are pressed in steel dies (30,000 psi) and sintered in vacuum from 2300 to 3500° F. TiC cermet compositions range from 20% up to 80% TiC. Molybdenum, tungsten, chromium and a solid solution (Ti, Ta, Ni) carbide are common additions to the binder metal. These additions influence the strength and oxidation resistance and the physical properties are controlled by the microstructure.

Alumina-chromium cermets have been developed for high temperature applications. The alumina used is a high purity, 99.5% corundum form. The average particle size should be less than 10 microns. Alumina-chromium powders are ball milled 180 hours in steel mills with tungsten carbide balls using methyl alcohol as the liquid medium. After drying and granulation, the material is hydrostatically pressed at 35,000 psi and sintered at 1700° C. (3100° F.) in a slightly oxidizing atmosphere of hydrogen. Compositions range from 28% wt. Al_2O_3 to 70% wt. Al_2O_3, the balance, chromium. Alumina-chromium cermets are stronger at high temperature than titanium carbide cermets and sustain this strength over a longer period of time, but are much more susceptible to failure by thermal shock and impact. In general, as the alumina content of the cermet is increased, the strength increases and the ductility, thermal shock resistance, and impact resistance decreases.

Thorium oxide is the basis for thoria-molybdenum cermets used to make cathodes for magnetron vacuum tubes. Thoria is a good thermionic emitter, has low vapor pressure and a high melting point (2800° C). Thorium oxide and molybdenum of average 2 micron diameter are preferred. The oxide and metal are mixed by ball rolling for 24 hours. Pressures used in forming, range from 5000 to 200,000 psi, depending on the shape. Sintering is accomplished at temperatures ranging from 1500° C. (2732° F.) to 2200° C. (3992° F.) in reducing atmosphere. Electrical resistance is an important property to permit proper heating in the application.

The thoria-molybdenum cermet must be used in a vacuum or protective atmosphere because it has no resistance to oxidation.

CHROMIUM ALUMINIDE. Chromium aluminide (CrAl) with the high melting point of 2160° C. has good oxidation resistance. Its thermal expansion is 10.0 x 10^{-6} per °C. Very little data on other physical properties or applications are available.

CHROMIUM BORIDES. These borides are formed by fusion of chromium and boron in the electric arc to form CrB or reaction of Cr_2O_3 and boron in the electric furnace. Five phases are found in the Cr-B system. Cr_2B is orthohombic, CrB also orthorhombic, CrB_2 hexagonal, Cr_3B_2 and Cr_3B_4 orthorhombic. All borides are stable against HF, HCl, HNO_3, H_2SO_4 and alkali solutions.

CrB_2 has a density of 5.6, melting point 2760° C., tensile strength of 106,000 psi., thermal conductivity 0.049 cal/sec/cm²/cm/° C. and a thermal expansion of 4.6 x 10^{-6} per °C. All borides are subject to oxidation the rate being very dependent on the temperature involved. CrB_2 has good oxidation resistance in the temperature region where B_2O_3 glass is stable. This glass forms as the oxidation product and protects the surface from further oxidation. This material has been used experimentally in rocket nozzle applications but thermal shock and oxidation resistance at high temperatures are not suited for the application.

CHROMIUM CARBIDE. A very hard, highly abrasion resistant material which also possesses excellent resistance to chemical corrosion.

Chromium carbides are usually sold as a finished product containing some nickel which serves to form a binder matrix. The material is also available in powder form.

Chromium carbides have hardnesses ranging from 86–89 Rockwell A. They are relatively low melting compared with other carbides, and have densities ranging from 6.5 to 7.0 g/cc. depending on the binder content. The coefficient of thermal expansion is about 6.0 x 10^{-6}° F., and the electrical conductivity is about 2.5% of copper.

Chromium carbides have tensile strengths of about 30,000 psi, modulus of transverse rupture is 100,000 psi, and the compressive strength is about 400,000 psi.

Chromium carbides are formed by standard powder metallurgical techniques, cold pressing and sintering. They can subsequently be finished to a hard, bright surface of high reflectivity and optical flatness.

Extreme hardness and excellent surface finish make these materials suitable for use as precision gage blocks. They are also being used in structural parts such as bearings, seals, valve seats, orifices, and, due to their resistance to corrosion, they are also finding use in chemical equipment service.

CHROMIUM SILICIDES. A series of hard, brittle, intermetallic compounds which have excellent resistance to oxidation in air at elevated temperatures.

Chromium silicides are available in powder from of fairly high purity. Stoichiometric compositions include Cr_3Si, Cr_2Si, $CrSi$ and $CrSi_2$.

Chromium silicides in general have similar characteristics, both physical and mechanical. Hardness ranges from 76–89 Rockwell A. Melting points vary from 1570° C. for $CrSi_2$ to 1710° C. for Cr_3Si, which has a cubic structure, A15 type, whose lattice dimension is a = 4.555 A°. X-ray density is 6.52 g/cc. $CrSi_2$ has a hexagonal, C40 type, lattice, the dimensions of which are a = 4.42 and c = 6.35 A°. X-ray density is 5.0 g/cc. Electrical resistivity varies from 23 micro-ohm-cm for Cr_3Si to 600 micro-ohm-cm for $CrSi_2$.

Chromium silicides have moderate strengths, depending on methods of preparation. Modulus of transverse rupture at room temperature ranges from 30,000–60,000 psi. At 1000° C. the corresponding values are 40,000–80,000 psi. Oxidation resistance in still air is excellent to 1100° C., thermal shock behavior is good, but resistance to impact loading is practically zero.

Chromium silicides can be formed by standard powder metallurgical techniques of hot pressing or cold pressing followed by a sintering operation.

High hardness coupled with oxidation resistance may make these materials useful as wear resistant components at elevated temperatures.

COBALT ALUMINIDE. CoAl. A hard, brittle, high melting intermetallic compound.

Cobalt Aluminide is available in powder form in sizes from granules down to a few microns average particle size. The material is fairly pure, equivalent to technical grades.

Cobalt Aluminide melts at about 1630° C., and has a fairly wide range of homogeneity. The crystal structure is body centered cubic with a = 5.86 A°.

COPPER TITANATE. $CuO \cdot TiO_2$. Mol. Weight 159.7—Approximate analysis 50.1% CuO, 48.9% TiO_2. Used as an addition to barium titanate types of capacitor bodies in amounts ranging from $\frac{1}{4}$ to 2% by weight. Promotes higher fired density of body.

DEHYDROABIETYLAMINE, technical grade. An amber, viscous liquid, insoluble in water but soluble in most organic solvents. Some ceramic inks, containing acidic resins (squeegee oils), are prone to change viscosity upon storage and will often set up into a hard mass. The effect is more evident if petroleum solvents are used in the inks. Addition of 2 to 5% dehydroabietylamine to the vehicle will stabilize the viscosity. Other advantages are good wetting and dispersing agent for the pigments, plus superior flow and levelling properties. The material also promotes adhesion of the color to glass. Aside from these uses, coordination complexes can be formed by reacting dehydroabietylamine with metallic salts. The reaction products can be applied to the formulation of conductive coatings for ceramics, "bright" golds, silvers, etc.

DEXTRIN. Three percent of yellow potato dextrin mixed thoroughly with dry body ingredients and then the whole mixed with 8% water, may be used for isostatic molding of specialty electronic components. The batch should be stored in sealed jars and allowed to age for one week to insure complete diffusion of the moisture.

DIAMOND POWDER COMPOUNDS—These are being used increasingly for certain types of fine finishing and polishing. These materials are used in finishing ceramic radomes, certain types of ferrites and in precision grinding of aluminum oxide bodies.

DIDYMIUM. Didymium materials contain about 45% lanthanum, 10% praseodymium, 33% neodymium, and small amounts of the other rare earths. Didymium materials are available as the carbonate, oxide, and many other types of compounds.

Didymium compounds are used in ceramic capacitors, and in many applications where rare earth materials are used.

DIP COATINGS. For ceramic electronic components are comprised of the phenolics, styrenes (polystyrene lacquers) and epoxy varnishes.

DYSPROSIUM OXIDE. Dy_2O_3, mol. wt. 372.9. Soluble in acids and only very slightly soluble in water. It is one of the rare earths. It is available in purities ranging from 95 to 99.9%. Due to its high thermal neutron cross section (1.100 barns/atom) it is of interest as a nuclear reactor control rod component, and as a neutron density indicator. In nuclear applications it is used as the oxide dispersed in stainless steel, or as the disilicide, etc.

It has a density of 7.81 gms/cc and has a cubic crystal structure. Has seven stable isotopes ranging from 0.05% to 28.2% and the major impurities are yttrium oxide and holmium oxide. In addition to nuclear ceramic applications, it is used in dielectric compositions, and as a special phosphor activator.

ENCAPSULATION. Materials for ceramic electronic components. See Polyvinyl Chloride and Epoxy Resin.

EPOXY RESINS are being used in electronic and new ceramics as adhesives, potting and casting materials and as coatings for encapsulation.

ERBIUM OXIDE. Er_2O_3, mol. wt. 382.4. Soluble in acids, only very slightly soluble in water. It is one of the rare earths. The oxide and salts of erbium have a beautiful pastel pink color. Erbium materials in high purity have been available only recently, and no significant uses have been developed. Potential applications is in rare earth garnets as ferrimagnectic materials for microwave electronics.

Er_2O_3 has density of 8.64 gms/cc and has a cubic crystal structure, and has six stable isotopes ranging from 0.136% to 14.9%. Major impurities are thulium oxide and holmium oxide. Uses include infra-red absorbing glasses, phosphor activator and as a nuclear poison.

ETHYL CELLULOSE. The cellulose ether resulting from the reaction of ethyl chloride and alkali cellulose. Possesses a great flexibility over a wide range of temperatures. Dissolves in many solvents and is tough and stable. Burns gently without leaving carbonaceous residues. The combination of these excellent physical and chemical properties explains why ethyl cellulose is used as a binder for certain technical ceramics and pigments. Also useful as a parting agent for thin sheet ceramics made by the so-called "Doctor Blade" method.

EUROPIUM OXIDE. Eu_2O_3, mol. wt. 352.0. Soluble in acids, and only very slightly soluble in water. It is one of the rare of the rare earths, and is available in purities of 95 to 99.9%. Its thermal neutron cross section of 4,600 barns/atom makes it attractive as a nuclear control rod. Such control rods are usually europium oxide cermets in stainless steel. Other uses are as phosphor and scintillation crystal activators.

Eu_2O_3 has a density of 7.42 gms/cc and a cubic crystal structure. It has two stable isotopes and the major impurities are samarium oxide and gadolinium oxide. Other uses outside nuclear ceramic applications include fluorescent glasses.

FERRITES. See SPINEL.

FERROSPINEL. See SPINEL.

GADOLINIUM OXIDE. Gd_2O_3, mol. wt. 361.8. Soluble in acids, only very slightly soluble in water. It is one of the rare earths, and is available in purities from 25 to 99.9%. It has the highest thermal neutron cross section of all the elements (46,000 barns/atom) and is potentially a useful nuclear control rod material. It forms garnets having useful ferrimagnetic properties. Gd_2O_3 goes through a crystal inversion at about 1300° C.

Gr_2O_3 has a density of 7.41 gms/cc and a cubic crystal structure. It has seven stable isotopes ranging from 0.20% to 21.9% and its major impurities are yttrium oxide and europium oxide. Besides its nuclear ceramic applications it is used in dielectric ceramics, vacuum tube filament coatings, special glass compositions and as a special phosphor activator.

Gd_2O_3 containing about 2% Terbium was sintered at 1500° C. in pressed compacts. Compacts had a density of 7.64 gm/cm^3 (theoretical density 7.60), modulus of rupture of 2840 psi; modulus of elasticity of 18 x 10^6 psi; linear thermal expansion (25 to 1000° C.) 10.5 x 10^{-6} in./in./°C.

GALLIUM ANTIMONIDE. GaSb. Mol. wt. 191.5. Melting point 705.9° C.

Crystallizes in zinc-blende structure. Crystals are hard, brittle, and of metallic appearance. Oxidizes readily in air at elevated temperatures. Prepared by melting together pure gallium and antimony under inert or reducing atmosphere. Subsequent zone-refining is necessary for high purity. Single crystals are grown by pulling from the melt. There is some reason to believe that gallium is soluble in the compound to the extent of about 1 part in 10^5.

GaSb is of interest as a semiconductor. Of the several Group III-Group V element compounds with semiconducting properties, GaSb most closely approximate germanium. The forbidden gap width is about 0.8 e.v. as compared with 0.75 e.c. in Ge. Both p-n junction and point-contact rectifiers have been prepared. However, no transistor effect has as yet been observed.

GALLIUM ARSENIDE. GaAs. Mol. wt. 144.6. Melting point 1240° C.

Crystallizes in zinc-blende structure. Prepared by melting together stoichiometric quantities of Ga and As in a sealed ampoule to prevent loss of As by volatilization. Purification by zone refining is also carried out in sealed ampoules. Fused silica containers have been successfully used. Single crystals may be grown by pulling from the melt .

GaAs is of interest for microwave diodes and high-temperature rectifiers and transistors. Its relatively large energy-band gap of 1.34 ev and electron mobility of about 12,000 cm^2/volt-sec at room temperature give this semi-conductor advantages over both germanium and silicon. The mobility of the positive carriers is about 650 cm^2/volt-sec. Recent progress in the purification of gallium and arsenic will greatly aid development work on devices requiring ultra-high-purity GaAs. Transistors made from GaAs have been produced in the laboratory.

GALLIUM PHOSPHIDE. GaP. Mol. wt. 100.7. Crystallizes in zinc-blende structure. Crystals are transparent with orange color. Prepared by melting together the elements in sealed silica tube and freezing slowly from one end.

GaP is of some interest as a semiconductor. The energy gap is about 2.56 e.v. at room temperature. The infrared absorption cut-off is at about 0.5 microns.

GERMANIUM. Ge. At wt. 72.6. Element No. 32. Melting point 958.5° C.

Density 5.32. Gray-white, brittle, metallic-appearing crystals with diamond structure. Prepared by reduction of GeO_2 by hydrogen or from certain ore residues by fractional distillation of its volatile tetrachloride, $GeCl_4$.

In addition to its use as the oxide (see GeO_2), germanium has recently assumed great importance in the electronic industry, as it is the material of what most transistors and many crystal rectifiers are made. For electronic use ultra-high purity, obtained by zone refining of the element reduced from high-purity oxide, is required. Apparent impurity concentration of of 1 part in 10^{10} have been obtained. Single crystals are prepared by drawing from the melt, to which has been added the required doping agents.

As a semiconductor germanium exhibits an energy gap of 0.75 e.v. and in the case of highly perfect crystals unusually long minority carrier life-times (up to 1 millisecond) together with relatively high carrier mobilities. Its chief limitation is the temperature limitation ($<100°$ C.) of operation imposed by the energy gap.

Germanium compounds analogous to the silicones are being explored.

GERMANIUM DIOXIDE finds its prime use in the role of being used in the high purity form as the source of Germanium crystals which are then used as semiconductors. However, germanium oxide complexes and solid solutions with good piezoelectric and ferroelectric properties are being investigated.

GLASS BONDED MICA. Recent developments by a company in this field have led to the production on a commercial basis of this unique material termed a "ceramoplastic."

Glass bonded mica is available in several grades for a wide variety of applications. It can be used at operating temperatures up to 650° F., and some grades can endure even higher temperatures.

There are several grades of glass bonded mica, each with its own combination of properties such as arc resistance, moldability. machinability, and dielectric constant (10 on up).

These materials, manufactured by bonding high temperatures glass frit with natural or synthetic mica, have an unusual combination of properties for high-temperature, high frequency electrical and electronics applications. Dimensional stability, arc resistance, excellent dielectric properties, moldability with or without metallic inserts, lack of mold shrinkage and resistance to radiation effects are featured, as well as high temperature endurance. Glass-bonded mica, made with natural muscovite mica, will withstand temperatures up to 750° F. when precision molded. Glass bonded micas made with synthetic mica, withstand continuous temperatures up to 850° F. (machinable) and 750° F. when molded. Another glass bonded mica can be molded like a plastic but will withstand continuous operating temperatures over 1100° F., and short time exposure to even higher temperatures.

Properties of Glass Bonded Mica

Electrical
Dielectric Constant 10^{10} cps... 6.9
Loss Tangent, 10^{10} cps... .003

Mechanical
Specific Gravity... 3.0
Flexural Strength, psi... 15,000
Modulus of Elasticity—psi... 11×10^6

Thermal
Maximum Operating Temperature
  Continuous, °F... 800°
  Short Time, °F... 1,000°
Specific Heat, cal/gm/°C... 0.17
Thermal Conductivity, cal/cm²/sec/(°C./cm)... .0012
Thermal Expansion... 11.2×10^{-6}

GRAPHITE. Natural graphite is mined in most parts of the world with the best sources being Ceylon, Canada and Mexico. Artificial or synthetic graphite is referred to as "graphitic carbon."

Graphites have a specific gravity of 2.1–2.5, Mohs hardness of $\frac{1}{2}$–$1\frac{1}{2}$ and a sublimation point of greater than 3500° C. It is unctuous; burns slowly; is chemically inert; flexible over a wide temperature range; good conductor of heat and electricity; is hydrophobic; has a negative coefficient of resistivity; tends to produce water in oil type emulsions and has excellent weathering properties.

It is used in clay bonded refractory applications in some cases glazed to prevent oxidation. As a mold material it is used to hot press many of the newer ceramic materials. Also finds uses as a coating material and in nuclear applications, either by itself or in ceramic compositions.

HOLMIUM OXIDE. Ho_2O_3, mol. wt. 377.9. Soluble in acids, only very slightly soluble in water. It is one of the rare earths, and is available in purities of 99 and 99.9%. It has become available commercially only recently.

Ho_2O_3 is available in buff colored granules or powder, has a cubic structure and its impurities are dysprosium oxide and erbium oxide. It is presently being used in special refractories.

HYDROABIETYL ALCOHOL. An ingredient in screen process media for the control of drying, flowout, and viscosity.

INDIUM ANTIMONIDE. InSb. Mol. wt. 236.5. Melting point 523° C. Crystallizes in zinc-blende structure. Crystals are hard, brittle, and metallic in appearance. Prepared by melting together the pure elements under neutral or reducing atmosphere. Further purification by zone refining is necessary for InSb intended for electronic applications. Single crystals are prepared by the technique of pulling from the melt.

InSb is of interest primarily as an infrared detector. The low value of the energy gap (0.18 e.v.) results in photoconductivity extending to about 8 microns in the infrared. In addition indium antimonide has an extraordinarily high electron mobility—up to 80,000 cm²/v-sec. at room temperature and up to 800,000 cm²/v-sec. at liquid nitrogen temperature.

Both p-n junction and point contact rectification have been observed. The low value of the energy gap, however, makes these rectifiers of little potential value at ordinary temperatures.

INDIUM ARSENIDE. InAs. Mol. wt. 189.7. Melting point 936° C. Crystallizes in zinc-blende structure. Prepared by melting together stoichiometric quantities of pure In and As in a sealed, evacuated silica ampoule. Purification of the resultant compound is accomplished by zone-refining.

InAs is of interest as a semiconductor. The energy gap is about .47 e.v., electron mobilities about 23,000 cm²volt⁻¹sec.⁻¹ at room temperature. Although the energy gap is too small to make InAs practical as a transistor material, this same property makes it of interest as an infrared photoconductor. The absorption cut-off lies at about 3.5 microns.

The relatively high mobility and the small dependence of the electrical properties on temperature makes InAs of particular interest for Hall effect and magneto-resistance devices. Such devices are currently available.

INDIUM PHOSPHIDE. InP. Mol. wt. 145.7. Melting point 1070° C. Prepared by heating indium to 1100° C. in a controlled phosphorus atmosphere in a sealed ampoule. Crystallizes in the zinc-blende structure. May be purified by zone refining. Caution should be used in the preparation of this compound because of the high pressure of phosphorus vapor over InP at the melting point of the compound.

InP is a semiconductor and is useful for rectifier and transistor applications. It has an energy band gap of 1.27 e.v. and an electron mobility of about 6,500 cm^2/volt-sec. The mobility of the positive carriers is extremely low (about 150 cm^2/volt-sec). InP was the first compound semiconductor to exhibit a useful transistor effect. It is one of the more promising materials for electronic devices to operate at intermediate temperatures.

INTERMETALLIC COMPOUNDS. By definition this class of compound includes the borides, hydrides, nitrides, silicides and aluminides of the transition metal elements of the 4th to 6th group in the periodic sequence, combined with semimetallic elements of small diameter. Investigations to date reveal over 1000 possible compounds with approximately 200 having melting points above 1500° C.

Methods of preparation for the silicides and aluminides are very similar to those used for carbides, nitrides and borides. These are (1) synthesis by fusion or sintering, (2) reduction of the metal oxide by silicon or aluminum, (3) reaction of the metal oxide with SiO$_2$ and carbon, (4) reaction of the metal with silicon halide or (5) fused salt electrolysis. The simplest method of preparation consists of mixing the metal powders in proper ratio, heating in vacuum or inert atmosphere to the temperature where reaction begins at which point the exothermic nature of the reaction furnishes heat for completion of the reaction.

The best forming methods are hot pressing and vacuum sintering. See compound listings this chapter.

IRON OXIDES. In ferromagnetic ferrites iron oxide is the basic constituent, generally comprising 50 to 80% of the ferrite batch by weight, and being reacted with other metallic oxides to form extensive solid solutions in the preparation of the final product. Ferrites in their final form crystallize in the cubic spinel structure and have the general formula MeFe$_2$O$_4$ where Me may represent Zn, Cd, Cu, Mg, Co, Ni, Mn, Fe or a mixture of these or other ions.

Synthetic iron oxides of the type manufactured for use as paint pigments are admirably suited for use in ferrites. These materials are ordinarily prepared by one of two methods: (1) the acid digestion of metallic iron with simultaneous oxidation and precipitation as hydrated alpha ferric oxide ($Fe_2O_3 \cdot H_2O$). This hydrate is dehydrated to produce alpha Fe_2O_3, or (2) by the roasting of copperas ($FeSO_4 \cdot 7H_2O$ to form alpha Fe_2O_3.

The acid digestion process characteristically gives an acicular particle and the roasting of copperas characteristically gives a particle more nearly spherodial. The acicular particle has low apparent density and high water demand whereas the spheroidal particle has higher apparent density and low water demand. Either of these products can be produced in a broad range of particle-size distributions with the smaller particle-size red iron oxides ordinarily being appreciably lighter in color than the larger particle-size iron oxides. In the lighter shades the particles are in general appreciably smaller than 1 micron. In ferrite production, because of the higher apparent density and lower water demand, the products prepared by roasting cooperas are generally used. The higher density reduces molding compression-ratios and enables the production of a more dense, free-flowing molding granule which fills the dies more uniformly, usually enabling also the use of lower pressures when pressing.

The solid impurities content of these materials may be less than ½%, with alkalis, alkaline earths, aluminum, silicon, titanium and transition elements as commonly occurring chemical impurities. The properties of the ferromagnetic spinel will be affected by both chemical and physical characteristics of the iron, depending upon the type of ferrite and its processing treatment.

LEAD BORATE. $Pb(BO_2)_2 \cdot H_2O$; mol. wt. 310.88. Anhydrous salt 94.2%, H_2O 5.8%, Pb 66.6%, PbO 71.8%, B 6.9%, B_2O_3 22.4%. **Poisonous** white powder, insoluble in water, soluble in dil. HNO_3. Used with other metals such as silver in galvanoplasty for the production of conductive coatings on glass pottery, porcelain and technical ceramics.

LEAD SILICATE. A large amount of work has been done on the applications of lead fluxed bodies of extremely high dielectric strength. The lead silicates and special lead frits have been used. A wide firing range for lead fluxed steatite has found commercial application.

LEAD METANIOBATE. $Pb(NbO_3)_2$. Forms ferroelectric yellow crystals with a 570° C. Curie point. Lead metaniobate is prepared by the reaction: $PbSO_4 + Nb_2O_5 \rightarrow Pb(NbO_3)_2 + SO_3$. The material can be polarized to obtain piezoelectric properties through the application of 50 volts per mil at 250° C. for 30 minutes. The lower sensitivity and dielectric constant of lead metaniobate, as compared with barium titanate, is more than made up by the wide latitude of temperatures over which it may be operated without depolarization. This high Curie point makes possible the manufacture of transducers, such as missile accelerometers, where high ambient temperatures can be expected.

LEAD METATANTALATE. $Pb(TaO_3)_2$. This material is reported to have ferroelectric properties.

LEAD SELENIDE. PbSe. Mol. wt. 286.2. Melting point 1088° C. Crystal structure, NaCl type. Very similar to PbTe, and like Bi_2Se_3, its apparent application is in the preparation of the Pb(Se,Te) type materials. The lattice parameter is 6.14 Angstrom units and the band separation (T = 300° K) is 0.26 e.v. Mobility (T = 300° K) for electrons is 1,200 and for holes is 600 cm^2/volt-sec.

LEAD STANNATE. Lead stannate, as prepared by precipitation from an aqueous reaction, is a photosensitive, light yellow powder, having the formula: $PbSnO_3 \cdot 2H_2O$. This compound is dehydrated by heating to 200° C. or above, leaving the anhydrous lead stannate, $PbSnO_3$ (M. W. −373.91).

Lead stannate, as an additive to barium titanate capacitor bodies, acts like the stannates of barium, calcium and strontium in that the temperature of the Curie peak is progressively lowered as the amount of lead stannate in the body is increased. Peak values of dielectric constant are not as high as for the bodies containing barium, calcium or strontium stannates but the peaks are considerably broader, giving rise to bodies of high dielectric constant with somewhat decreased variations with temperature change.

Lead stannate, added in amounts of 1–5 per cent by weight to barium titanate bodies intended for piezoelectric applications, greatly reduces the tendency of these units to depolarize under load when used as oscillators.

Other stannates available for study: cadmium, cobalt, copper, ferric, ferrous, manganous and zinc.

LEAD TELLURIDE. PbTe. Mol. wt. 334.9. Melting point 920° C. Crystal structure, NaCl type. PbTe is usually prepared by the direct reaction of the elements in a quartz or graphite boat under a hydrogen atmosphere.

As PbTe retains its semiconducting properties to approximately 400° C. it is one of the leading candidates for thermoelectric power generation. The lattice parameter is 6.44 Angstrom units and band separation (T = 300° K) is 0.3 e.v. Mobility (T = 300° K) for electrons is 2,000 cm^2/volt-sec and for holes is 1,100 cm^2/volt-sec.

LEAD TITANATE. $PbTiO_3$. Mainly used as an addition agent for ferroelectric barium titanate bodies to improve the piezoelectric properties. One such body is:

BaTiO₃... 96% by wt.
PbTiO₃... 4% by wt.

Recently there have been important discoveries made in the lead titanate/lead zirconate system. A very useful composition contains 45% lead titanate and 55% lead zirconate. The Curie temperature of this body is 340° C. compared with barium titanate's 120° C. See United States Patent 2,708,244, *Piezoelectric Transducers Using Lead Titanate and Lead Zirconate,* dated May 10, 1955, and Re. 24,191, reissued July 31, 1956. Within the range of possible compositions of lead titanate and lead zirconate may be found bodies which have a higher dielectric constant, piezoelectric activity and primary transition temperature than possible heretofore with barium titanate.

LEAD ZIRCONATE. $PbO \cdot ZrO_2$. Used as a component in piezoelectric bodies, lead zirconate and barium—lead zirconate bodies constitute a class of ferroelectrics having dielectric constants as high as 11,000. Lead zirconate and lead titanate compositions ranging from 50 to 55 mol percent of each are used for piezoelectric applications which have excellent electro mechanical properties and which are stable over a wide temperature range.

LECITHIN. (Vegetable or soybean lecithin.) An emulsifier; lowers surface tension. Of great value to silk-screen media (conductive silver paints, etc.). Added as a 25% solution in pine oil.

LITHIUM BOROSILICATE. Used extensively in high temperature corrosion resistant coatings. Also in mixtures with lithium fluoride in coating compositions.

LITHIUM METATANTALATE. $LiTaO_3$ Curie point, above 450° C. (ilmenite structure?), because of low crystal symmetry single crystals are required in studying the ferroelectric properties of this compound.

LITHIUM TITANATE. *In ceramic insulating bodies* based on titanates, lithium titanate is preferred as a flux because of its stability.

LITHIUM ZIRCONATE. In ceramic insulators and capacitors based on zircon and zirconates, lithium zirconate by reason of its thermal stability, has proved of considerable value as a flux.

Soluble in acids, only very silghtly soluble in water. It is the last member of the rare earth series, and is available in purities up to 99.9%. It has recently become commercially available.

LUTETIUM OXIDE. Lu_2O_3. White powder with mol. wt. 397.98, and cubic crystal structure. The material is insoluble in water but soluble in all common acids. It has two stable isotopes at 97.4% and 2.6% and the major impurity is ytterbium oxide.

MAGNESIUM STANNATE. Magnesium stannate, as prepared by precipitation from an aqueous reaction, is a white powder, having the formula: $MgSnO_3 \cdot 3H_2O$. The water of hydration may be driven off by heating to 340° C. or above, leaving the anhydrous magnesium stannate ($MgSnO_3$, M. W. −191.02). The anhydrous compound may also be prepared by a solid state reaction between $MgCO_3$ and SnO_2.

Magnesium stannate finds use as an additive to barium titanate bodies designed for capacitor applications. By addition of magnesium stannate the Curie peak of barium titanate is depressed and for small additions of magnesium stannate, the general level of dielectric constant is increased at temperatures below that of the Curie point. Thus, bodies of moderately high values of dielectric constant (about 2,000) may be obtained which show relatively little change with temperature (less than 25% total over the range from room temperature to 85° C.) through the use of a 1 to 3 mole percent addition of magnesium stannate to barium titanate.

Magnesium stannate has also been recommended for use as a phosphor base.

MAGNESIUM TITANATE. A low dielectric constant material (K 13 to 17) which has a positive temperature coefficient of capacity (100 to 120). It can be used by itself or in combination with heavy grade TiO_2 or barium titanate for capacitor applications. As an addition to heavy grade TiO_2, its function is to lower the dielectric constant and the T. C. of capacity. As an addition to the barium titanate and high K bodies, its function is to act as a depressant of the dielectric constant at the Curie temperature.

Magnesium titanate bodies are prepared in the same manner as barium titanate compositions. If the parts are dry pressed, slightly lower pressures may be used (6,000–8,000 psi) and in addition, when firing, slightly lower firing temperatures are employed (2,250° to 2,350° F.).

The dielectric constant measured at 1 kc remains quite stable from −60 to +20° C. From 60 c/s to 10^8 c/s, the dielectric constant is also stable.

At room temperature the power factor varies slightly in the frequency range 60 to 10^8 c/s. With higher temperatures the power factor deviates more markedly over the above frequency range.

Magnesium titanate has the lowest density of all the titanates (powder form—2.2 gm/ss.; fired—3.10 gm/cc.). Its thermal expansion curve is linear over the temperature range 80° C. to 320° C.

MAGNESIUM ZIRCONATE. $MgO \cdot ZrO_2$. Unlike the other alkaline earth zirconates, no compound of magnesium zirconate is formed. It is commonly used with other dielectric materials in the range of 3 to 5% to obtain dielectric bodies with special electrical properties. A body composed of 95% barium titanate and 5% magnesium zirconate (by weight) has a dielectric constant of about 2,000 at 24° C., and 2,200 at 60° C. and 2,000 at 85° C. Beyond this, up to 140° C., the dielectric constant drops quite rapidly, being about 1,000 at 140° C. Its function is to depress the dielectric constant at the Curie temperature.

MANGANESE. Pure electrolytic manganese metal is being investigated by basic ferrite researchers. It is a pure source of manganese for sintering into ferrite structures. The high degree of chemical purity allows broad property modification through areas requiring minimum contamination or controlled impurities.

MANGANESE OXIDE. In ferromagnetic ferrites manganese oxide is used as one of the primary constituents of the zinc-manganese type, where it may be from 10 to 30% of the composition by weight. Manganese is also one of the major constituents of computer memory core ferrites, and in other types it may be used in minor quantities to obtain property modifications.

A variety of grades and types of manganese compounds are utilized, ranging from high-grade ores to highly purified synthetic chemicals. Some of the common forms of the manganese materials are MnO_2, Mn_3O_4, $MnCO_3$ and the hydrated oxides. In general, material with a fine particle size and a high degree of chemical purity is desirable, some of the more commonly occurring chemical impurities being alkalis, alkaline earths, iron and silica.

MELAMINE FORMALDEHYDE. A condensation product of melamine and formaldehyde. Melamine formaldehyde rosins when cured to a thermoset state have good arc resistance, dielectric strength, and are resistant to elevated temperatures. They are used as bonding agents for fibrous glass insulation where resistance to burning at elevated temperatures is desired. Fiber glass bonded with melamine is used to make electrical panels and parts.

MICA. Synthetic mica has recently been put into commercial production and is available in various powdered forms, in organically bonded paper sheets, in a three dimensional hot pressed machinable synthetic mica ceramic, and in sheet form of limited area. Synthetic mica has unusually high thermal stability; for example, a synthetic fluor-phlogopite can be safely used at temperatures up to 1,800° F., whereas muscovite mica, the most common commercial variety, is limited to temperatures below 1,100° F. An investigation now under way promises to produce a flexible synthetic mica with excellent electrical properties and high heat resistance and flexible at elevated temperatures. See "Glass Bonded Mica" this section.

MOLYBDENUM ALUMINIDE. Mo_3Al is one of the higher melting aluminide compositions, 2,150° C. Its thermal expansion is 7.7 x 10⁻⁶ per °C. Although its oxidation resistance is poor in comparison to other aluminides and silicides, it is good in comparison to molybdenum metal. Shapes may be fabricated by hot pressing or vacuum sintering techniques. Crucibles have shown promise for the melting of titanium metal.

MOLYBDENUM DISILICIDE. A hard, refractory intermetallic compound. Its outstanding resistance to oxidation in air at temperatures up to 1,700° C. makes it potentially useful for high temperature applications. Molybdenum disilicide is commercially available in high purity powder in various sizes down to −325 mesh.

Molybdenum disilicide has a hardness of 80–87 Rockwell A. Its melting point is approximately 2,000° C., but there is some decomposition at the melting point accompanied by appreciable silicon loss. The crystal structure is tetragonal, 011b type, with dimensions a = 3.20 and c = 7.86 Å. X-ray density is 6.24 g/cc. Electrical resistivity at room temperature ranges from 21–27 micro-ohm-cm, depending on the method of fabrication. The coefficient of thermal expansion is 8×10^{-6} ° C.

Molybdenum disilicide is fairly strong, but not at all resistant to impact loading. Fabrication methods have great influence over strengths, but modulus of transverse rupture runs from 40,000 to 60,000 psi. Compressive strength varies from 100,000 to 350,000 psi. Appreciable strength is retained at least up to 1,200° C. Stress to rupture at 1,000° C. in 100 hours, is 13,500 psi.

Molybdenum disilicide can be formed by powder metallurgical techniques such as hot pressing, or cold pressing and sintering. It can also be cast, but this is complicated by decomposition at the melting point. Ingots are porous and have very large grain size. The powder can also be formed into parts by slip casting and sintering, but this technique, while well known in the ceramic industry, is a relatively new concept which has only lately been applied to metal powder fabrication.

The excellent resistance to oxidation at high temperatures, combined with fairly good elevated temperature strength makes $MoSi_2$ promising for elevated temperature structural applications where impact resistance is not a major consideration. Several possibilities are gas turbine nozzles, blades, and other parts subjected to similar service, furnace heating elements, and a metal ceramic combination of $MoSi_2$ and Al_2O_3 has been considered for use as kiln furniture, saggers, sand blast nozzles, hot draw or hot press dies, and induction brazing fixtures.

MORPHOLINE. $NH(CH_2)_2OCH_2CH_2$. About 12 cc. per gallon of water will act as a rust inhibitor for steel machinery when wet-grinding or lapping ceramics. May also be used as an emulsifying agent for ceramic binder preparations.

NICKEL ALUMINIDE. An intermetallic compound whose resistance to oxidation, combined with its high melting point, make it potentially useful as a high temperature structural material.

Nickel aluminide is available commercially in powder form in various mesh sizes from granular material to an average particle size of a few microns. The material is stoichiometric NiAl and is of a fairly high purity.

Nickel aluminide has a hardness of about 68–72 Rockwell A, and a melting point of 1640° C. The crystal is body centered cubic, a = 2.88 Å, and the X-ray density is 6.05 g/cc. Electrical resistivity at room temperature is 25 micro-ohm-cm. The coefficient of thermal expansion is 15.1×10^{-6} ° C.

Nickel aluminide is fairly strong at room temperature with modulus of transverse rupture values ranging from 30,000–140,000 psi, depending on fabrication methods. Some slight yield is noted during these tests. At 1,000° C., the corresponding values are approximately half the room temperature strength. Creep resistance at these temperatures is extremely poor. Thermal shock is quite good, passing NACA standard tests.

Nickel aluminide can be formed by hot pressing or by cold pressing and sintering, but the former method produces by far the best results.

Excellent oxidation resistance and fairly good strength might make this material considered for turbine blading or other combustion chamber applications. It has impact resistance which is better than most ceramics, intermetallic compounds, and some cermets. NiAl is also resistant to attack by molten glass, and red and white fuming nitric acid, which suggest possible uses in the glass processing industry or in some high temperature chemical processes.

NICKEL BONDED TITANIUM CARBIDE. A hard, strong material which retains its strength at temperatures up to 1,100° C. It is the most commonly used of the so-called cermet materials for high temperature structural applications.

Nickel bonded titanium carbide is available in powder form, although common practice is to purchase finished parts from the manufacturer. Variations in purity of the carbide (carbon content) and amount and type of binder material make the number of grades available quite large.

Nickel bonded titanium carbides have hardnesses ranging from Rockwell A 80 to Rockwell A 89, depending on the binder content. The melting point is that of the binder material, and the density varies from 5.0 g/cc upward, depending on the amount and nature of the binder material. Thermal conductivity is in the range of .04 to .07 cal/cm-sec-°C. Thermal expansion coefficients are on the order of 8 to 10 x 10^{-6} °C. Electrical resistivity varies from 60 to 80 micro-ohm-cm.

Nickel bonded titanium carbide is usually made by cold pressing and sintering methods, but it can be hot pressed and, if the binder content is very high, it can even be cast.

The material may be used for turbine blading, in high temperature structural applications, as tool bits, and, a more recent application, as a high temperature bearing and seal material, where high compressive strength, low coefficient of friction, and high wear resistance is needed at elevated temperature. Oxidation resistance of these materials is fair and can be improved somewhat by adding niobium or tantalum carbide to the hard phase or by adding cobalt or chromium to the nickel binder. The large number of variations of the straight nickel bonded titanium carbide have been developed as a result of studies aimed toward improving one property or another, and in order to determine which material is best for a particular application, a consultation with the carbide manufacturer is probably necessary.

NICKEL OXIDE. In ferromagnetic ferrites nickel oxide is one of the primary constituents, along with zinc oxide and iron oxide, used in forming the nickel-zinc type of ferrite. The quantity in a batch may vary from 3 to 25%, and in television core applications one or more bivalent metal oxides in addition to nickel and zinc are usually incorporated in the material to obtain the required properties. Nickel oxides and carbonate of fine particle size and a high degree of chemical purity are desirable for ferrite applications, these requirements being determined by the type, end use and processing treatment of the product. Cobalt, iron, alkalis, alkaline earths, copper and silica are commonly occurring impurities.

NICKEL STANNATE. Nickel stannate, as precipitated from an aqueous reaction, is a light green powder of the formula: $NiSnO_3 \cdot 2H_2O$. Upon heating to above 125° C., the water of hydration is removed, leaving the anhydrous compound $NiSnO_3$ (M. W. -225.39).

Nickel stannate has been suggested for use in barium titanate capacitor bodies where it behaves in a manner similar to magnesium stannate, when the two are compared on a molar basis.

NIOBIUM OXIDE. And the niobates of sodium, cadmium and other common elements have been found to possess ferroelectric properties, many of the combinations having Curie temperatures from 200–275° C.

NITROPARAFFINS. An important group of compounds which can be used in formulations for the electrophoretic deposition of ceramic materials for various technical ceramic applications. Cermet coatings may be produced from formulations containing carbides and silicides which are electrophoretically co-deposited with a reducible metallic oxide. Ceramic enamels and metallic oxides can be deposited using the same techniques. Of widespread application is the electrophoretic deposition of alumina on electronic tube parts—for example, as a non-emissive electrical insulation on heaters.

OCTYL ALCOHOL. Used as an aid in de-airing casting slips. Also as a wetting agent for ball mill batches, consisting of a 5% solution of Aerosol OT in octyl alcohol. Add 1 cc. of this solution to each 100 grams of solids in the slip.

POLYACRYLAMIDE. A substitute for gum arabic, British gum, starch, dextrin, and other thickening agents. A good dispersing agent.

POLYVINYL CHLORIDE RESINS. The dispersion types of resins are used in flexible molding compounds. Such formulations consist of (1) a vinyl paste resin, (2) a suitable plasticizer such as dioctyl phthalate, and (3) a stabilizer (usually a compound of lead). Flexible molds are widely applied to plaster casting and encapsulation of electronic circuits with epoxy resins.

POTASSIUM FLUORIDE. Used in the preparation of ferroelectric barium titanate crystals having an improved rate of remanent polarization decay. KF is used as a flux in a six-hour heating cycle to 1,150° C. After cooling the KF is dissolved with water.

POTASSIUM METATANTALATE. $KTaO_3$. Material crystallizes with a perovskite structure with a Curie point of 13.2° K. The dielectric constant has a maximum value of >4,000 at the Curie temperature.

SAMARIUM OXIDE. Sm_2O_3. Mol. wt. 348.70 with a cubic crystal structure, and density of 7.43 gms/cc. It is very slightly soluble in water and soluble in all common acids. It is a white powder with slight yellow cast and as impurities it contains small amounts of neodymium oxide, europium oxide, and gadolinium oxide. Samarium oxide has seven stable isotopes ranging from 3.1%, 15.0%, 11.2%, 13.8%, 7.4%, 26.8% and 22.7% and in addition to its nuclear uses is used in luminescent glasses, infrared absorbing glasses and as a phosphor activator.

A sample of 99.9% pure sample of the material, compacted and sintered at 1,500° C. to a 99% of the theoretical density (7.43 gm/cm^3) had a modulus of rupture of 2,000 psi; modulus of elasticity of 25.6 x 10^6; coefficient of linear expansion between 100° and 1,000° C. of 9.9 x 10^{-6} in./in./°C. The material was unstable in boiling water but similar bodies fired to 1,300° C. to 81% of theoretical density were stable in boiling water.

Equimolar mixes with Fe_2O_3 were magnetic and have the advantage over metallic magnetic materials in that they are not conductors and therefore are not heated by stray currents in a fluctuating magnetic field.

Sm_2O_3 has a high thermal neutron cross section of 6,500 barns per atom, making it usuable as a nuclear control rod material. The material is also used as a phosphor activator.

SILICON. Si. At. wt. 28.06. Melting point 1,420° C. Sp. gr. 2.42. Second most abundant element, but occurs only in compounds, never in the free state. It is a gray-white, brittle, metallic-appearing element, not readily attacked by acids except by a mixture of hydrofluoric and nitric acids. Soluble in hot NaOH or KOH. It is prepared in the pure crystalline form by reduction of fractionally distilled $SiCl_4$.

By far the largest use of silicon is as compounds in the ceramic industry. It is also employed as an alloying agent in ferrous metallurgy, and as the basis of the family of chemicals known as silicones.

A relatively recent application of silicon is in the electronics industry, where it has been widely employed in the manufacture of crystal rectifiers. More recently, sufficiently pure silicon has been produced by carefully controlled zone refining and crystal growth to make possible its use as transistors. Since the energy gap in silicon is 1.1 e.v. compared to 0.75 e.v. for germanium, silicon transistors may be operated at higher temperatures and power levels than those made of germanium.

SILVER. Silver is used in conductive coatings for capacitors, printed wiring, and printed circuits on titanates, glass bonded mica, steatite, alumina, porcelain, glass and other ceramic bodies. These coatings are also used to metallize ceramic parts to serve as hermetically sealed enclosures as integral sections of coils, transformers, diodes, etc.

Two types of conductive coatings can be used on ceramic parts: those that are fired on and those that are baked on or air dried. The fired on type contains, in addition to silver powder, a finely divided low melting glass powder, temporary organic binder, and liquid solvents; in formulations having direct soldering properties and others suitable for electroplating, both having excellent adhesion and electrical conductivity. The baked-on and air dry types contain, in addition to silver powder, a permanent organic binder and liquid solvents, in preparations having somewhat less adhesion, electrical conductivity and solderability than the fired on type, but which can be electroplated if desired. The latter type is used when it is not desirable to subject the base material to elevated firing temperatures.

Any of the above silver compositions are available in a variety of vehicles suitable for application by squeegee, brushing, dipping, spraying, bonding wheel, roller coating, or any other specific technique or equipment requirement.

Firing temperatures for direct solder silver preparations range between 1,250–1,450° F. Silver compositions to be copper plated are fired at 1,200–1,250° F. The firing cycle used with these temperatures will vary from 10 minutes to 6 hours, depending upon the time required to equalize the temperature of the furnace charge.

A solder composed of 62% tin, 36% lead, 2% silver is generally used with the direct solder silver compositions. It is recommended that this solder be used at a temperature of 415–425° F. Soldering to the plated silver coating is less critical and solders composed of 50% tin, 50% lead or 60% tin, 40% lead, as well as other soft solders, are being used with good results.

The air dry silver compositions will, as the designation implies, air dry at room temperature in approximately 16 hours. This drying time can be shortened by subjecting the coating to temperatures of 140–200° F. for 10–30 minutes. The baked on preparations must be cured at a minimum temperature of 300° F. for 5–16 hours. The time may be shortened to one hour by raising the temperature to 575° F.

TABLE III

Magnetic moment of some ferrospinels
Magnetic moment (Bohr magnetors)

Ferrite	Observed	Computed (spin only)
$MnFe_2O_4$	5.0	5
Fe_3O_4	4.2	4
$CoFe_2O_4$	3.3	3
$NiFe_2O_4$	2.3	2
$CuFe_2O_4$	1.3	1
$MgFe_2O_4$	1.1	0
$Li_{0.5}Fe_{2.5}O_4$	2.6	2.5
$ZnFe_2O_4$	0.0	0

TABLE IV

Magnetic moment of zinc substituted ferrites

$Me_{1-a}Fe_2O_4$	a = 0	0.1	0.2	0.4	0.6
Mg	1.1	2.0	(2.8)*	(3.5)*	(1.7)*
Ni	2.3	2.9	3.6	4.8	(4.8)*
Co	3.3	3.9	(4.3)*	....	....
Fe	4.2	(4.7)*	(5.2)*	(5.7)*	(5.7)*
Mn	5.0	5.5	5.8	6.2	....
$Li_{0.5+}Fe_{0.5}$	2.6	3.3	3.8	4.4	3.0

* Values in parentheses were taken from curves.

TABLE V

Properties of some ferrospinels

Ferrite	Mo (approximately)	Curie temperature (°C.)
$CuFe_2O_4$	90	410
$CoFe_2O_4$	1.1	520
$FeFe_2O_4$	70.0	590
γ-Fe_2O_3	....	620 (extrap)
$LiFe_5O_8$	30	590
$MgFe_2O_4$	60	325
$MnFe_2O_4$	250	290
$NiFe_2O_4$	30	580

The same soft solders and techniques as recommended for the fired on coatings may be used for the electroplated air dry and baked on preparations. It is extremely difficult to solder to air dry or baked on coatings without first electroplating.

The surface conductivity of the fired silver coating is far better than that of the air dry or baked on coating. Fired coatings have a surface electrical square resistance of approximately 0.01 ohm while the surface electrical square resistance of air dry or baked on coatings is approximately 1.0 ohm.

SODIUM METATANTALATE. $NaTaO_3$. This material is ferroelectric, crystallizing in a perovskite structure and shows a Curie point of 475° C.

SOLDER, HARD. Also **Silver Solders.** Alloys, usually containing silver, that melt at temperatures above 700° F. They produce joints that are short only of welding in strength. Wire-wound resistors are made by winding a resistance wire on a non-feldspathic steatite core, and then silver-soldering the ends of the coil to copper terminal straps. The resistor is given a protective and insulating coating of porcelain enamel.

SOLDER, SOFT. Alloys that melt below 700° F. Principally alloys of lead and tin. Used in the assembly of ceramic electronic components such as capacitors, transducers, and printed circuits. There are about 30 common alloys commercially available but the most widely used one is the tin/lead eutectic composition (63% tin, 37% lead). Where ceramic-bonded, silver electrodes are involved, a 62% tin/36% lead/2% silver composition insures that the electrodes will not be scavenged by the molten solder.

SPINEL. $MgO \cdot Al_2O_3$ or $MgAl_2O_4$. A compound finding limited use as an electrical insulator. The magnetic spinels have recently skyrocketed in importance because of the widespread interest and application of the ceramic ferrospinels (ferrites). Two classes of ferrospinels occur: the magnetic and non-magnetic. The magnetic are related to the "inverse" structure and the non-magnetic to the "normal" structure.

Magnetite (Fe_3O_4) is the parent of all the ferrospinels with all or part of the ferrous ions (Fe^{2+}) replaced by one or more divalent cations as Mg, Cu, Mn, Co, Ni, Cd and Zn. The last two form "normal" spinels and are non-magnetic, however they are important in enhancing the magnetic properties of the magnetic spinels. The magnetic ferrospinels have the "inverse" cation arrangement or some variation between that and the normal arrangement, depending upon the particular compound and the heat treatment it was subjected to.

Neel has described the origin and magnitude of the magnetic moment in the ferrites. A strong electron spin alignment of the electrons in the magnetic ions (3-d electrons of the transition metals) within each site and an antiparallel alignment between different sites leads to a net moment due to the uncompensated spins. Gorter has determined these values for various ferrites: Zinc ferrite is a "normal" spinel (non-magnetic) with the zinc ions occupying the tetrahedral sites. Adding zinc ferrite (or cadmium ferrite) to the magnetic ferrospinels gives a lattice with more magnetic ions in the octahedral sites, thus a higher magnetic moment.

The ferrites are generally prepared by reaction between component oxides and are processed by standard ceramic techniques. Pigment manufacturers and some chemical suppliers make some of the ferrite powders available, however most component manufacturers prefer to make their own. The special care required to maintain the high purity of the material and the skill needed to achieve the desired homogeneity in the final product makes it necessary to control all steps closely from the initial oxides to the sintered piece. Useful electrical and magnetic properties can be varied widely by the processing techinques, therefore no tabulation of these properties can be regarded as representative. In addition, the industrial products are rather complex combinations which vary markedly from the ideal ferrospinels discussed above. Their greatest utility has come in replacing less efficient metals at high frequencies.

STEARATES. A class of organic materials used chiefly as dry type lubricants for the dry pressing of technical ceramic products. Stearates, including those of aluminum, calcium, magnesium and zinc are used. They give some internal lubrication during forming plus a small increase in bonding strength but their prime function is better lubrication of the die.

STEATITE. Refers almost entirely now to electrical insulators made from talc. Formerly, the term referred to the massive type of talc mineral which could be machined to close tolerances, then fired. Due to a decreasing market and a shortage of supply, this terminology is almost unheard of any more. Powdered talc has been successfully bonded with materials such as magnesium oxychloride or phosphorus cement acid so as to form dense machinable blocks which may in time find a market value.

STRONTIUM STANNATE. Strontium stannate, as prepared by precipitation from an aqueous reaction, is a white powder, having the formula: $SrSnO_3 \cdot 3H_2O$. The hydrated compound dissociates upon heating to 400° C. or above, leaving the anhydrous strontium stannate ($SrSnO_3$, M. W. −254.33). The anhydrous compound may also be prepared by a solid state reaction between a strontium compound, e.g., $SrCO_3$ and SnO_2.

Strontium stannate is used as an additive in barium titanate capacitor compositions in which its function is similar to that of barium stannate. (See under Barium Stannate.)

Effect on the shift of the Curie temperature is a linear function of the percent addition made. Approximate analysis, SrO 39.1%, SnO_2 58.2%, ignition loss 1.3%.

STRONTIUM TITANATE. Strontium titanate is a high dielectric constant material (225–250) which at lower temperatures has a temperature coefficient of dielectric constant somewhat higher than calcium titanate.

Strontium titanate bodies can be dry pressed (6,000–8,000 psi) or slip cast and are fired to vitrification at a peak temperature of 2,450° to 2,550° F.

Strontium titanate can be used by itself or in combination with barium titanate in applications for capacitors and other parts.

The power factor of strontium titanate is unusually high at low frequencies with a great improvement in power factor in the neighborhood of 1 Mc/s.

The thermal expansion of strontium titanate is linear over a wide temperature range (100° to 700° C).

STRONTIUM ZIRCONATE. $SrO:ZrO_2$. Used in the dielectric compositions in amounts from 3 to 5%. Strontium content results in the shift of the Curie temperature to a lower value.

TALC. In general, the grade of talc used in making steatite electrical insulators has low alumina, low iron, and low calcium. Where a forsterite type of development is desired, magnesium oxide or magnesium carbonate may be added. Likewise, in making this type of steatite insulator, it is common to make minor additions of barium carbonate and clay as auxiliary fluxes. This type of body is also frequently bonded with the newer types of organic resins. Major production of talc for the electronic field now comes from Montana and in general are of the massive type.

TANTALUM OXIDE and the tantalates of sodium, cadmium and other common elements have been found to possess ferroelectric properties, many of the combinations having Curie temperatures from 200 to 275° C.

TERBIUM OXIDE. Tb_4O_7, mol. wt. 748.8. Soluble in acids, only very slightly soluble in water. As ignited in air, the oxide has the composition Tb_4O_7, but other terbium compounds are related to the sesquioxide Tb_2O_3 (mol. wt. 366.4). It is one of the rare earths and is available in purities up to 99.9%.

Tb_4O_7 is a chocolate colored powder with a mol. wt. 747.72 and cubic crystal structure, and its major impurities are terbium oxide and gadolinium oxide.

THORIUM OXIDE. A spark plug insulator composed of a mixture of aluminum oxide and 6 to 50% thorium oxide are known.

Thorium oxide is the basis for thoria-molybdenum cermets used to make cathodes for magnetron vacuum tubes. Thoria is a good thermionic emitter, has low vapor pressure and a high melting point (3,200° C.). Thorium oxide and molybdenum of average 2 micron diameter are preferred. The oxide and metal are mixed by rolling for 24 hours. Pressures used in forming, range from 5,000 to 200,000 psi, depending on the shape. Sintering is accomplished at temperatures ranging from 1,500° C. (2,732° F.) to 2,200° C. (3992° F.) in reducing atmosphere. Electrical resistance is an important property to permit proper heating in the application.

The thoria-molybdenum cermet must be used in a vacuum or protective atmosphere because it has no resistance to oxidation.

THULIUM OXIDE. Tm_2O_3, mol. wt. 386.8. Soluble in acids, only very slightly soluble in water. It is one of the rare earths, and is available in purities of 99 and 99.9%. Its primary use is as a radiation source, after irradiation in a nuclear reactor, in portable X-ray equipment.

TITANIUM CARBIDE. A very hard, refractory material, finding increasing usage for wear-resistant applications and for applications requiring material with good thermal shock resistance.

Titanium carbide is available in both very high purity grade and technical grade. The difference between the grades is largely a matter of carbon content. Granular material and powder in various sizes down to average particle size of a few microns can be obtained.

Titanium carbide has a hardness about equivalent to that of silicon carbide, a melting point of 3,140° C. and density of 4.93. It is relatively strong (bending strength: 20,000 psi, compressive strength, 109,000 psi) and has a thermal expansion of 74×10^{-8}. Its thermal conductivity is 0.041 cgs (less than half that of silicon carbide).

Titanium carbide can be formed either by bondless hot pressing or by powdered metallurgy techniques.

The material is finding use as components in cermets such as jet engine blades and cemented carbide tool bits.

Titanium carbide has a relatively low electrical resistivity (1×10^{-4}) and can be used as a conductor of electricity, especially at high temperatures.

Extreme hardness of titanium carbide makes it suitable for wear-resistant parts such as bearings, nozzles, etc. It also serves for special refractories under either neutral or reducing conditions.

See Cermets, this chapter.

TITANIUM DIBORIDE. TiB_2, mol. wt. 69.54; density 4.52 gms/cc; melts at 2,920° C.; Knoops hardness (K100)—2,710; electrical resistivity at room temperature 15.2 micro-ohm-cm. Insoluble in HCl and HF. Reacts with hot H_2SO_4 and in soluble in $HNO_3-H_2O_2$ or $H_2SO_4 \cdot HNO_3$ mixtures. It is prepared by: (1) Reacting titanium and boron in the solid state. (2) Fused salt electrolysis of melts containing boric acid anhydride, and oxide of magnesium or calcium, a fluoride of magnesium or calcium, and TiO_2. (3) Reaction of TiO_2, Ti, or TiC with B_4C. (4) Fusion of titanium with boron in an arc or high frequency vacuum furnace. (5) Reaction of TiO_2 and B_2O_3 in the presence of carbon.

In recent years considerable interest has been shown in TiB_2 because of its refractoriness, hardness and electrical properties. It may be fabricated into very hard, dense objects by hot pressing or it may be used in powder form as a component of cermets. The TiB_2 and bonding metal are compacted in the powdered state and sintered in controlled atmospheres.

TiB_2 has become available in commercial quantities fairly recently although there is not widespread use of this material. However, there is an increasing amount of research being conducted on TiB_2 with applications in mind such as the following: special refractories; wear resistant items such as anvils, gages, and guides; bearings or bearing liners; cutting tools; jet nozzles or venturie; crucibles; arc or electrolytic electrodes; resistance elements; high temperature conductors of electricity; contact points; hard facing welding rod coatings; and metallurgical addition agents.

TITANIUM DIOXIDE. TiO_2. Available in three mineral forms: rutile, anatase, and brookite; distinguished from each other by differences in crystal modification, index of refraction, density, etc. Only the rutile form is used for dielectric purposes.

Rutile bodies are used in either the pure form or with minor additions of various materials for: capacitors (substitutes for mica, paper, and electrolytics), temperature compensating (tc) capacitors, trimmer condensers, by-pass condensers, filter and power circuits, and as fillers for resins and low melting glasses.

Manufacture involves dry mixing or tempering with water (up to 10%), dry pressing at 5,000–10,000 psi., or extrusion, or for complex parts, slip casting (deflocculate with 1% ethylene diamine or 1% tannic acid with 10% NH_4OH), followed by firing the parts to vitrification with approximately a two hour soak at peak temperature (2,400–2,450° F.). Results have shown that in firing titanium dioxide bodies a particular fired structure yields the best all around dielectric properties and may be obtained in a body having a porosity of zero or nearly zero.

As a capacitor, pure rutile has a dielectric constant of 173 parallel to the principal axis and 89 perpendicular to this axis. Most polycrystalline bodies produced commercially have a value of 85–95 at room temperature when measured statically or in the frequency range of 60 cycles/sec. to 3,000 megacycles/sec. Bodies are characterized by a fairly large negative coefficient of dielectric constant 750–800 (25–85° C.) which may be made less negative by the addition of other compounds such as magnesium titanate or zirconium dioxide (though with a decrease in dielectric constant).

Power factor is roughly 0.5% to 0.7% at 60 cycles/sec., dropping off rapidly to 0.05% at 10^4 cycles and remaining at that figure to 10^9 cycles. Resistivity (25° C.) is approximately 10^{-14} ohm-cm for commercial grade TiO_2 and 10^{-16} to 10^{-18} ohm-cm for extremely pure TiO_2. Ordinary dielectric strength is 150 to 200 volts per mil, but proper design of the test piece can raise this to 600–700 volts/ml for commercially pure TiO_2 and about 50% higher for very pure TiO_2.

Temperature compensating capacitors based on TiO_2 have dielectric constants varying from 15 to 85 and temperature coefficients varying from $+ 120 \times 10^{-6}$ through zero to -750×10^{-6}. (Most negative body has highest TiO_2 content.) The compensators are necessary in all radio recivers where the exact frequency of resonance of the resonant circuit changes slightly with changes in temperature. These undesirable changes are corrected by introducing a reactive component having a temperature coefficient of the opposite sign and of such a value as to offset the undesired change with temperature. Extraordinary duplicable and close tolerances are available, in some cases as accurate as 3 to 5 parts per million. Capacities range from 1 to 1,100 uuf.

Trimmers or trimmer condensers employing TiO_2 bodies are used for minute adjustments of occasional nature of capacity. The parts are made with extreme accuracy. Normally the rotor consists of a TiO_2 body which is usually supplied in one of three temperature coefficient types, and the base is a low loss ceramic composition.

Physical properties of TiO_2 bodies include relatively low strength (modulus of rupture—18,000–22,000 psi., tensile strength—6,000–8,000 psi.) low thermal conductivity (0.149 cal(cm/sec/° C.), and a coefficient of expansion (for rutile) of $7–9 \times 10^{-6}$.

TITANIUM SILICIDE. Compound formed by reaction of the metal powders, having formula Ti_5Si_3. Has high melting point of 2,120° C., theoretical density 4.2. Excellent oxidation resistance at elevated temperatures. Its extreme brittle nature prohibits its use alone as a high temperature material when application involves thermal shock.

TUNGSTEN TRIOXIDE. WO_3. Single crystals of this material of good purity are reported to show ferroelectric properties at liquid air temperature.

URANIUM CARBIDE. Both the mono (UC) and the di (UC_2) are being investigated for nuclear fuel element possibilities.

URANIUM DIOXIDE. Currently being used as a nuclear fuel element when metal clad. Also being used in the enriched from and in combination with ThO_2. UO_2 uses are now confined exclusively to nuclear application and work on the ceramic cladding of these materials is under investigation.

URANIUM NITRATE. Another uranium compound under investigation for nuclear application, and no longer available to the ceramic industries for previous uses.

WAXES. Microcrystalline waxes, such as Cerese AA, are used for the vacuum impregnation of inorganic filled, organic bonded, electrical insulating coatings for ceramic capacitors and other electronic components. The wax is chosen because of its low moisture permeability.

A 6% solution of a mixture of tri- and tetrachloronaphthalines in carbon tetrachloride has been used as a dry-press binder for certain technical ceramics. It may also be used as a capacitor impregnant.

Wax emulsions shuch as S/V Ceremel C and X have been widely used as binders for dry press mixes and glaze suspensions. A high melting point paraffin will also make an excellent binder for dry-press granules. The paraffin is melted, added to the body, and then thoroughly incorporated by means of a heated, muller-type mixer.

Ordinary paraffin can also be used to bond ceramic parts to steel plates for attachment to magnetic chucks during grinding and lapping operations. After the components are ground to the desired size, they can be removed from the plates quite easily with hot water.

YTTERBIUM OXIDE. Yb_2O_3, mol. wt. 394.1. Soluble in acids, only very slightly soluble in water. It is one of the rare earths, and is available in purities up to 99.9%. It has recently become commercially available.

A white powder with a density of 9.17 gms/cc, it has a cubic crystal structure. Yb_2O_3 has seven stable isotopes ranging from 0.14%, 3.03%, 14.3%, 21.8%, 16.2%, 31.8% to 12.7% and has thulium oxide and lutetium oxide as impurities. It is finding use in dielectric ceramic bodies.

YTTRIUM OXIDE. Y_2O_3, mol. wt. 225.9. Soluble in acids, only very slightly soluble in water. It is extracted from rare earth ores, although it is not a rare earth. It is available in purities ranging from 75 to 99.9%.

ADDENDUM

MATERIALS AND CONTROL FOR HIGH PRECISION STEATITE

Available in a myriad of shapes ranging in size from pinpoint to 14 inches by 5 inches, precision dielectric ceramics manufactured by the National Ceramics Co., Trenton, N. J., represent one of the most exacting operations in the ceramic industry today.

Known as "Natite," these products are fabricated under standard tolerances of $\pm 1\%$ of the dimensions involved, but not under $\pm .005$ inches, whichever is greater. Closer tolerances can be adhered to through additional material controls and precision grinding to tolerances of $\pm .002$ inches, when requested.

In addition, these ceramic parts can be metalized for special applications where mechanical holding, hermetic sealing or electrical connections are to be made with low temperature solder directly to the ceramic piece.

Body Preparation and Control

High quality talcs of uniform properties are the foundation upon which precision steatite manufacture rests, and only certain talcs have proven desirable over a long period of time. So necessary is close control in the batching operation that each body batch is numbered and "pedigreed" from its origin. The body, the quantity of moisture, and quantity and type or types of binder are recorded on an identification card which remains with that batch in process.

Use Magnetic Separator

Upon opening the bags of materials, all material is passed twice through a dry-type magnetic separator, after which the batch is weighed out and passed twice through a comminutor. This breaks down agglomeration and develops homogeneity of the batch. To the dry materials, water and binder (in solution) are added at a precise quantity after a fixed period of dry Lancaster mixing. A longer period of mixing follows, allowing sufficient time to uniformly distribute water and binders so that homogeneity is achieved.

The batch, now in a plastic condition, is processed through a comminutor which yields plastic granules of the 10- to 20-mesh range. At this stage the material can be wet pressed on Dennison presses exactly like electrical porcelain. The plastic granules are likewise ready for extrusion. De-airing under high vacuum gives high green strength and density.

Stamped for Identification

Each length of extruded stock is stamped with a number identifying the body batch, die size, pin size and binders. A sample quantity from each

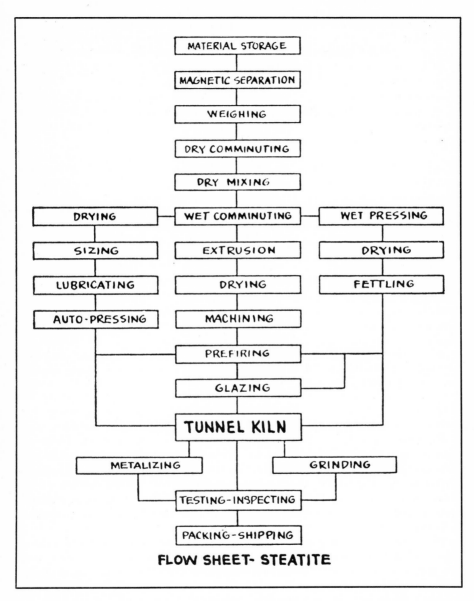

FLOW SHEET - STEATITE

extrusion run is dried to zero moisture and measured with a micrometer. Inside and outside diameter and length are recorded, the sample fired through the tunnel kiln, and the same measurements are made on the fired piece.

From these data, the fired shrinkage peculiar to the batch is determined. Shrinkage differs from batch to batch and also from one extrusion die size to another. In general, the diameter shrinkage is twice as much as the length. Dimensions on blueprints are factored by the shrinkage data and the dry stock is machined to these expanded dimensions. Tolerances of plus or minus one-thousandths of an inch can be held in this process. When tolerances are measured in ten-thousandths, after-fire grinding or lapping is required.

Dry Pressing Procedure

Automatic or dry pressing requires a different treatment of the wet granules. These are dried back to zero moisture, run through a bank of vibrating screens, and various sized fractions are recombined in designated proportions for specific jobs. To the dry granules a lubricant such as stearic acid is added and mixed thoroughly in a ribbon-type mixer. At this point the material is ready for pressing. Again shrinkage data must be obtained where very close tolerances are required. Accuracy within plus or minus one-thousandth of an inch is commercially possible in this process.

When glazing is required, much of the steatite must be prefired to burn out the organic binders. Skillful glaze spraying is essential in holding tight dimensional tolerances.

Firing Characteristics

The firing again calls for precision. The firing treatment of the machined piece must of necessity duplicate the firing of the shrinkage sample if close dimensions are to be met. Steatite, unlike the classic clay-flint-feldspar body, has no skeletal structure of flint to hold its shape at the maturing temperature. Rather, it is largely made up of highly viscous glass from which clino-enstatite crystallizes as the temperature lowers. Unless a piece is of good, self-supporting shape, vast deformation takes place. When by chance a batt breaks and drops in the hot zone, a flat steatite piece will conform to the broken parts of the batt as though it had the consistency of a rubber sheet. Steatite bonds to steatite so tenaciously at the maturing temperature that pieces stacked one upon the other fuse into one common unit.

This property is exploited in making some difficult shapes by stacking and fusing several easily shaped portions—the final result for all practical purposes being an integral unit. The tenacious fusion to itself and to alumina-bearing materials brings about a kiln furniture problem. The latest solution provided by refractory manufacturers is a silica carbide batt coated with zircon; zircon being inert at the maturing temperatures of steatite.

Rigid Inspection

Dimensional inspection is rigid to a degree seldom found in ceramics outside of the dielectric field. Gages are used where possible, but the micrometer is the universal tool. The majority of plant personnel are as familiar with micrometers and blueprints as the average person is with a fork and a newspaper. A good deal of the success in the manufacturing of precision ceramics results from the high degree of skill and reliability developed in the personnel.

Rigid control exerted by everyone in production pays dividends in low rejections during final inspection, and in turn rigid final inspection assures a minimum of rejects from customers.

Electrical properties are constantly being checked on a Boonton Q-Meter, Type 260-A. A constant search for improved dielectric compositions parallels the production effort at National Ceramic where the first 6L wollastonite body was developed.

INDEX